To

Mr. A. G. Striegel

with the compliments

of the author.

Wm. Kurrelhaus

New York

November 1950

The author in his research laboratory.

COATING and INK
RESINS

A TECHNOLOGICAL STUDY

by

Dr. WILLIAM KRUMBHAAR

President, Krumbhaar Chemicals, Inc.
South Kearny, N. J.

REINHOLD PUBLISHING CORPORATION
330 West Forty-Second St., New York 18, U.S.A.
1947

Printed in U.S.A. by
Haddon Craftsmen

Contents

List of Illustrations

Introduction

Since the Author's book, "The Chemistry of Synthetic Surface Coatings,"* was published, the group of synthetic resins on which surface coatings were then based, has undergone important development and expansion to the point that a separate discussion of coating and ink resins has become of great value. The field has actually spread to an extent that, in order to make

a practical and useful contribution

to the industry, the Author has found it necessary to limit the scope of this book to those resin types which are now in common use and with which he is in daily contact through development and production work. In this way, generalities and speculations which have no immediate bearing on the subject are avoided, and the discussions are based on practical experience only.

No reference is made to elementary chemistry, chemical equations or elaborate structural formulae, all of which mean relatively little in practical resin chemistry. The deeper the investigator goes into this field, the more he realizes that it is impossible to apply the ordinary conceptions of organic chemistry to resin chemistry. An alcoholic hydroxyl group, for instance, which, under other circumstances, behaves entirely as such, may not show its characteristics at all in the resin kettle; or a new, well defined substance with individual characteristics may have been formed in a resin reaction, and it still may be utterly impossible to develop analytical evi-

* Published in 1937 by Reinhold Publishing Corporation, New York, N. Y.

dence that a chemical reaction has taken place. Many of the resin reactions are borderline cases which reach over into the colloidal field.

This book endeavors to supply

the theoretical background

of the chemistry and physics of the resinous materials, as far as such conceptions can be supported by experimental evidence. Unfortunately, much is still to be left to more or less reasonably well founded guesses. But, as the resin man knows, instinct and experience often point to the real truth and, regardless as to whether confirmation or denial follows, the discussion of the chemical and physical mechanisms involved has been useful, because it will have provided some food for thought, or may have supplied some helpful working hypothesis. Wherever possible, simple experiments and determinations have been designed to interpret certain reactivities, and special emphasis is laid on a detailed description of methods of chemical analysis useful in resin technology. Such methods have been derived from long established procedures for oil and fat analyses and are far too little known among resin producers and users.

The comments on resin chemistry bring out clearly the fact that chemical research and development in this field are only in their initial stages and that systematic research will open up new grounds. Advertisements and promotion literature on synthetic resins traditionally boast about their miraculous new achievements. However, viewing the situation soberly there is

not too much reason for contentment

in the protective coating and printing ink fields. Consider, for instance, accomplishments in the rubber industry through development work which stepped up, within less than twenty years, the service life of an automobile tire at least fifteen times. No resin has as yet been found that will lengthen the life of a protective coating to anywhere near that extent. Or, consider the improvements in rust resistance of steel, which has been made practically perfect through very small additions of other elements. No such claims can be made for the weather resistance of surface coatings, not even on the basis of very large additions of reinforcing substances.

The scope of the text is confined to the light colored, hard, soluble and high viscosity groups of phenolic, maleic and copal type synthetics, all of which show interesting chemical re-activities when incorporated into surface coatings and printing inks. Since it is one of the main objects of this book to describe resin activities from this standpoint, resins of an inert character and resins which are handled in solution, are not included in the discussion.

The reception given the Author's book, "The Chemistry of Synthetic Surface Coatings," by the chemical public and the comments made at the time, have pointed out the type of information that is needed on resin technology. The chemists working with synthetic coating and ink resins in production, laboratory or application, need a reasonable conception of the basic principles underlying the formation of the resins and want a clearly defined picture of the chemical changes going on in the varnish kettle, when resins and oils are cooked together. This knowledge enables the varnish and ink chemist to intelligently conduct and modify his own manufacturing procedures, and removes him from

the class of varnish cooks

who used to mix the ingredients in their varnish kitchen according to some old inherited recipe, and left the rest to good luck. This information also provides the chemist with a good base for judging his own finished product and for selecting the right resin for the right purpose. From this point of view the present volume on the technology of coating and ink resins is written for the men who come into contact with such resins in production, testing, research, application or in patent work.

This book endeavors to report on resin technology in an open frame of mind, reservations being made only in highly specialized items. Secrecy has never been the attribute of success or progress. As experience has shown in many cases, the real reason for secrecy was the necessity for concealing the fact that there was nothing to conceal.

The first requirement to form a reasonable opinion on resin reactivities, is a somewhat detailed conception of the

size and shape of the resin molecules

and their arrangement in the internal resin structure.

Into the majority of coating and ink resins, rosin or rosin components are introduced in various ways and, therefore, knowledge of structure and chemistry of rosin and rosin esters is necessary. In spite of a large amount of scientific literature, far too little is known about rosin from a structural point of view, about the differences between abietic acid and commercial rosin, the questions of molecular weight and composition, the peculiarities of its carboxyl group, about anhydride formation and speed of saponification and esterification. The problem of double bonds in rosin and rosin esters has also remained a very controversial subject. Special attention, therefore, is directed to an elucidation of all these points.

Coating and ink resins discussed in this book are pure phenol resins, rosin-modified phenol resins, rosin-modified maleic resins and copal-type synthetics. Considerable experimental evidence has been assembled to make clear the internal structure of these resins.

It appears that oil-soluble pure phenolic resins are comparatively low molecular compounds of simple structure, the acid-condensed resins being even less complex than the alkali-condensed. Rosin-modified phenolics appear to be substantially two phase systems, consisting of a strong elastic framework of a pure phenol resin embedded in the rosin component. A discussion of the maleic resin build-up proves their structural analogy to alkyd resins generally. The development of copal-type synthetics has produced new and interesting conceptions on degradation and depolymerization of resins.

New techniques for the improvement of modified phenolics and maleics to be used for coating and ink purposes, have been developed. In these techniques the resins, after their formation is completed, are subjected to a

process of maturing

the physical and chemical details of which are of extreme practical interest. The changes in molecular weights, melting points, solubilities, acid and iodine values, saponification speeds and heat stabilities during resin maturing, indicate important structural rearrangements, effecting a thorough homogenization and stabilization of the resins.

Internal structure of resins and their physical properties are closely related to the molecular weights of the resins. In fact, the molecular weights are excellent characteristics for resin evaluation. They have hitherto not been used for this purpose because no reliable method of their determination was available. Such a method has now been developed in the Author's laboratories, yielding values which can be checked within 1-2%. An experimental investigation of the

molecular weights of coating and ink resins

reveals the interesting fact that the order of their molecular magnitude places them among the low polymers and definitely not among the high polymers and supplies information which is of unusually great interest in the theory and practice of resin technology.

The fundamentals of resin chemistry supply an excellent base for a discussion of resin oil reactivities, as they occur in varnish cooking. The conceptions in this field have been largely of a theoretical and speculative nature and require clarification by a serious consideration of the actual facts. It appears that chemical

reactions between resins and oils

are highly desirable to obtain good bodying, stability and drying properties of the varnishes and enamels and to obtain the necessary chemical resistance and mechanical characteristics of the dried film. It also appears that these effects depend on a number of chemical reactions, which heretofore have not been well established. The reactivities of the oils as such, as well as those of their decomposition products, is discussed in detail, particular attention being paid to the much debated and, certainly much over-rated problem, of interchange esterification.

The previously mentioned views on resin structure and reactivity apply generally to the three resin groups discussed in this book, *i.e.*, the phenolics, maleics and copal-type synthetics. In addition, each resin has its own individuality in its chemistry and physics and, therefore, is considered individually. In order to make such comments reasonably precise, limitation to a small number of representative resin types is necessary.

The technological aspects of

phenolic coating and ink resins

have always been governed by the tendency of the chemists to explain, by orthodox chemical reactions, the unique properties of phenolics. A conscientious investigation of these phenomena reveals that many of these ideas are illusions, created by wishful thinking. The chapter on phenolics bases its interpretations on the plain facts brought out by laboratory and factory experiments. The nature of the phenolic substituent, its position in the phenol ring, the type of the catalyst and the amount of formaldehyde used in the phenol formaldehyde condensation, are of paramount importance for the resulting pure phenol resins or rosin modified phenolic resins. The comments give the reasons why the resins dealt with in this book are limited to certain alkyl phenol, and bis phenol resins.

Research, based on correct determination of molecular weight gives a clear insight into the internal structure of phenolic resins and explains their high degree of reactivity as being due to the comparatively small molecular size. A discussion of the mechanism of the formation of both alkali- and acid-condensed resins brings out new and unusual concepts, based on a separate investigation of the phenolic and alcoholic hydroxyl groups. A few basic rules have been developed from this study, governing the reactivities of the pure phenolics with oils and, at the same time, throwing a very informative light on the chemistry of modified phenolics. It has been proved that modified phenolics possess reactivities which enable them to link up chemically with oils during the varnish cooking process.

The group of maleic resins is more diversified than generally assumed. The three basic components of rosin, polyhydric alcohol and polybasic acid can all be varied and changed independently in type, quantity and method of incorporation with the result that several dozen distinctly different resin types are possible. The chemistry of

maleic resin formation

has remained vague, due to the tendency of basing the reactions on orthodox chemical formulae, and using for explanation the mechanism of the diene reaction. This traditional legend has been kept up in spite of the fact that experimental evidence does not seem to confirm the diene mechanism. The chemically pure rosin maleic acid is prepared and investigated with regard to its chemical structure, its molecular weight, its basicity and its reactivities, leading to a better understanding of maleic resins generally.

The technological highlights of

the copal-type synthetics

are new and unique processes of depolymerization. They produce resins which closely resemble fused fossil gums in the mechanism of their formation and their internal structure, and which combine the advantageous properties of natural gums with the valuable characteristics of synthetic resins. The starting points for these products are materials that have a tendency to gelatinize and which, if gelatinized, can be again degelled. For certain purposes, copal-type synthetics are combined with natural gums which have been solubilized by a process of mastication, as described in a string of the Author's patents. In this procedure, the copal is subjected to powerful pressure in milling or kneading machines and thereby is considerably improved in fusability, solubility, and reactivity. The mastication process, apart from being of great practical importance, is of considerable theoretical interest, because it shows the possibility of influencing chemical properties by mechanical means. Interesting experimental evidence has been assembled to clarify the complex chemistry of copal-type synthetics.

Structure and reactivity of coating and ink resins form the base for their

technological property characteristics

which cover chemical characterization, melting point, viscosity, solubility, oil combination, and the problems of drying, gloss and film resistance. The methods for the determination of resin constants are common knowledge. They are described in that old standby reference book of Dr. H. A. Gardner's, "Physical and Chemical Examination of Paints, Varnishes, Lacquers, Colors." There are, however, a number of tests pertaining to the coating and ink resins exclusively which are discussed in detail in this volume.

Most of the resin property constants are interrelated in certain ways. Traditional resin-making practice considers such constants as being bound together firmly in a fixed order. For instance, it is customary to assume that viscosity is inversely proportional to solubility; or, that the melting point is directly proportional to viscosity. Modern resin production methods have taught that many resin constants can be disconnected from the traditional bonds and combinations of resin properties in nearly any variety can be created at will.

In discussing chemical characteristics of resins, interesting aspects are brought out with regard to resinous acids and anhydrides, and the saponification of their esters. Commenting on the possibilities of accurate chemical resin analysis, their very limited scope becomes painfully clear. Questions of melting point and viscosity embrace a number of controversial points calling for the elucidation of the method of their determination, such as the influence of speed of heating on the melting point and of false body on the viscosity. The relationship of resins and solvents involves the behavior of the resins with weak solvents, their tendency to crystallize, their compatability with other substances and their peculiar ability to keep volatile solvents in solid solution, a characteristic not always fully understood.

The process of

combining resins and oils

involves many important questions, such as the resin solubility in oils, the heat stability of resins, and requires the discussion of the practical significance of bodying speeds of resin oil combinations in all its ramifications. Of particular interest, from the resin point of view, are the ever present problems of after-bodying, pigment stability, skinning and bronzing.

A number of theoretical conceptions and practical view-points are discussed as to the process of film formation, and special importance is attached to the particular problems connected with printing inks. The influence of resin properties on printability, as expressed by tack measurements, and the role played by resins in overprint varnishes and high gloss inks, were objects of a comprehensive experimental study.

The durability and weather resistance of surface coating films are governed by the film resistance against oxidation, water action and mechanical influences. The destructive factors of oxidation and hydrolysis can be greatly reduced by resins; the action of mechanical forces is more involved and requires special resins to counteract their destructive effects. A study of tensile stress and strain conditions in films tells a highly enlightening inside story of durability, and as a result a good idea is obtained as to how to reinforce surface coatings mechanically and chemically through the proper use of synthetic resins.

The practical rules for

improving the durability

of protective coatings under severe climatic conditions will particularly interest our paint and varnish friends in Great Britain, Canada, India, Australia, New Zealand, and in Switzerland. Because of climatic conditions, they have to take the problem of weather resistance more seriously than is done in America. The British tradition simply demands finishes of long life, in spite of the climatic conditions. The English climate frequently has winter and summer all in one day, produces heavy pea-soup fogs, aggravated in their effects on surface coatings by salt dust or acid gases. Climatic conditions in Australia are characterized by excessive sun irradiation, not easy to cope with in protective coatings. The most difficult conditions are to be met with in the climate of India, where the amount of water vapor filling the air is so large that it is even a problem to keep cigarettes, cigars and matches in usable condition for only a few hours.

A clear understanding of the principles governing the formation, the reactivity and the technical properties of coating and ink resins is the base for the proper selection of resins for specific purposes and for

the practical formulative work

involved in utilizing resins for particular applications. A special chapter covers the practical aspects of resin applications in the field of surface coatings and printing inks, and should be of assistance to the sales service chemist in the paint and ink industry, as well as to the purely commercial sales force in the industry. Such information might help to make the chemist a better salesman, and the salesman a better chemist.

The comments on resin application should also be of assistance to the chemists in those activities which are consuming protective coatings and printing inks. Such industries include the building of aircraft, ships and vessels, railroad and street cars, automobiles and buses; they comprise the industries of paper, textiles and leather, of furniture, of containers and packages. They also include the making of electrical, communication, industrial and agricultural equipment. To make this discussion practical, the amazingly large number of resins on the market is reduced to a very few resin types of well defined composition, giving the important applications to which they are best suited, due to their individual characteristics.

Resin technology comprises more than the chemical angles of manufacture and practical application. It has to cover also the mechanical aspects of the equipment and machinery, and the legal aspects of the patent situation. The former comments interest the engineers, the latter ones the patent department, and both furnish valuable information to the executive who co-ordinates the work in plant, laboratory and office. The handling of such co-ordination is a sphere of activity all its own, like that of a ship's captain. In fact, the spirit prevailing in many of our enterprises is that of a ship's crew. People get the feeling that they are all sailing together in the same boat, with captain, officers and crew being busy day and night, and certainly looking askance upon any luxury passenger who might try to come along.

In describing the

engineering viewpoints of resin technology

emphasis is laid on the equipment and machinery which might directly interest the user of coating and ink resins, particularly the varnish producer. It is generally admitted that the mechanical equipment of the varnish industry has become antiquated, because in too many places it has not developed beyond the open fire and movable kettle stage. With the idea in mind to benefit the varnish maker in modernizing his machinery and equipment, some revealing details of modern resin production facilities are given, as, for instance, details on the arrangement of the machinery, the design and material of the kettles, the control instruments, apparatus for pressure and vacuum, refluxing and condensing, and devices for loading and unloading.

As the most vital factors, the methods of heating and cooling are discussed. The majority of resin producers today have adopted the indirect system of heat transfer by means of Dowtherm, because it allows rapid heating and cooling, thereby accelerating the production cycle and increasing the output in weight. In contrast to this system, heating by electricity is a slow process. Because many reactions of resin formation require ample time for completion, this slowness of electrical processing has its special merits for the production of the very best resins, and while its cost at first glance seems excessive, there are many advantages which do not appear on the surface.

As mentioned before, resin technology includes the patent problem, *i.e.* the general

questions of patent validity

and the particular questions of individual patents. It appears that the spirit which governs resin matters in the Patent Office and the Courts is somewhat different from the trend in other technical fields. The intimate knowledge of this spirit is of paramount importance for the patent men or the chemists, who enter the field of coating and ink resins and their practical application in protective coating and printing materials. To convey this information, a number of outstanding cases are discussed which, by Court hearings and final decisions, have greatly influenced the resin and allied industry. Fortunately, the industry as a whole benefited through general technical and scientific education from such legal fights to a greater degree than even the victorious party. The number of individual patents in the field of coating and ink resins is legion, and the quality of far too many of them is considered poor by most technical men. Within this field, the present comments confine themselves to the highlights of the patents on ester resins, soluble phenolics, maleics and copal-type synthetics, and are particularly concerned with those patents that have been held valid either by Court decision or by general approval of the industry.

After having absorbed all this information, the patent man will be in a good position to decide such questions as: whether a suggested application should be made, or a new process, planned by the production department, could possibly infringe on some other patented process, also, as to whether an outside patent can be deemed reasonably strong to justify royalty payments if demanded, or the starting of an infringement suit.

A discussion of costs and expenses involved in patent suits may also prove of value, as well as the outline given for a standard pattern for the proper styling of applications. These few remarks will sufficiently clarify the practical importance of the chapter on the patent situation.

All through the book, wherever possible, the comments are enlivened by

descriptive illustrations

some in color, reproduced from kodachrome photographs, others made with polarized light according to an especially developed technique. Such pictures will assist in enhancing the vivid impression which the reader obtains of the stimulating and even romantic spirit prevailing in the resin field.

Sensing this very spirit, the reader might be tempted to hurry through the volume in one session. After that, however, the book should be kept handy on the shelf for detailed study and continuous reference. In this way, this book will

help in the making of good finishes

and, as an old English saying goes "good finishes make good friends." But please bear in mind that this volume is not a chemical textbook, but a technological study. It does not know all the answers, but strives to incite the asking of a great many questions. If, in doing so, it stimulates an exchange of opinions and renders research more useful to the creation of better products, it has fulfilled its purpose.

Dr. William Krumbhaar

New York, N. Y.
    1947

FIGURE 1.   A rosin-modified phenol resin.

Chapter I

Chemical Fundamentals of Coating and Ink Resins

The resins discussed in this volume are pure phenol resins, rosin-modified phenolics, rosin-modified maleics and copal-type synthetics. The discussion is limited to resins which are to be used for surface coatings and printing inks and the comments are restricted to resins of high melting point, heavy viscosity, pale color, and good color stability, and possessing complete solubility in volatile solvents and drying oils.

These resinous materials have a beauty all their own, vested in color and transparency, which is brought out convincingly by the color photograph of a rosin-modified phenol resin, in *Figure 1.*

THE INTERNAL RESIN STRUCTURE

The majority of the resins under consideration are rosin-based resinous esters, containing phenol-formaldehyde condensates, maleic type compounds, solubilized copals, and polyhydric alcohols. Only a few of the resins are pure phenolics or non-esterified products. In the manufacture of all of the ester resins under discussion, substantial amounts of gum rosin, wood rosin or polymerized rosin are used. *Figure 2* gives an idea of how the most important of these rosin types, *i.e.* the gum rosin, is gathered by the tapping of pine trees, and shows a prospector looking over a future source of rosin supply in the swampy pine timber lands of Florida.

The commercial rosin, as it is used for coating and ink resins, has little similarity to

the pure abietic acid

with which it is customarily associated. The abietic acid can be obtained in pure form from resin by dissolving the rosin in three times its weight of petroleum ether, precipitating the rosin acids as amino abietates by adding butylamine and filtering off the precipitate. The amino salt,

FIGURE 2. Gathering gum rosin from virgin pines.

after being washed with solvent, is then suspended in petroleum ether, and diluted sulphuric acid is added to the suspension, whereby the pure abietic acid is set free, dissolved in the petroleum ether.

For the chemically pure acid, a molecular weight of 300 has been determined with an accuracy of plus/minus 10, which is in accordance with the customary formula for abietic acid isomers. The acid is highly oxidizable and takes up oxygen quickly, even if stored under water which has been boiled air free and has been saturated with carbon dioxide. Its melting point is extremely high, *i.e.* close to 190° C., but declines rapidly when the substance is heated beyond its initial melting point.

The molecular weight of the fused rosin acid is found to be considerably higher than 300 and continues to grow to more than 500, but not beyond 600, on further heating, indicating that the fusion causes the single molecule to form dimolecular units.

It is this

dimolecular form

in which the major part of rosin acids is present in commercial rosin. Molecular weights of 520 to 540 are determined for all types of commercial rosin, *i.e.* for pale and dark grades of gum or wood rosin, and also for the so-called commercial abietic acid. These figures allow the conclusion that in all cases, about three-quarters of the rosin is present in dimeric and only one-quarter in monomeric form. It is possible to raise the dimolecular portion up to practically complete dimerization by heat and vacuum treatment at a temperature below the temperature of decomposition. For instance, a sample of rosin with a molecular weight of 525 reached a value of about 600 after being heated at 260° C. for 18 hours, with vacuum applied during the last six hours.

The linkage between the two single molecules is of a stable nature, and is not subject to easy dissociation, as appears from the method used for molecular weight determination. This method determines the depression of the freezing point of diphenylamine, caused by the addition of varying amounts of rosin. The relative depression is the same whether 10%, 5% or 1% of rosin is dissolved, showing that even strong dilution does not separate the double molecules into single units. The molecular linkage in the dimeric parts of commercial rosin, however, is different in nature from the internal association, which is the base for the commercial types of polymerized rosin.

The molecular weight of

polymerized rosin

varies between 625 and 650, *i.e.* is only slightly higher than that of ordinary rosin. Since the degree of molecular association is not substantially higher, the characteristics of polymerized rosin must be explained by a different type of linkage, in which more reactive points are involved, rendering the bond firmer and more complex. This conception is supported by the fact that the iodine value of polymerized rosin is considerably lower, and its acid value is clearly lower than the figures for ordinary rosin.

Determinations of molecular weights have established the fact that the major part of the rosin acids present in commercial rosin exists in dimolecular form and possesses two carboxyl groups per molecular unit. This conception is supported by the observations made when

rosin in solution

is neutralized with calcium hydroxide. Using up to 6% calcium hydroxide for neutralization, *i.e.* half of the theoretical quantity, a pale and low viscosity solution of limed rosin is obtained. Employing more than 6% and up to the theoretical neutralization equivalent of 12%, a dark and high viscosity solution is obtained. The change in characteristics is very pronounced at the half-way mark and indicates clearly the existence of a well defined acid calcium resinate, as can be expected from a dimolecular rosin acid.

Generally speaking, dimolecular monobasic acids are not unknown in organic chemistry. Acetic acid, for instance, can exist in a dimolecular form. It is also known that the monobasic oleic acid is able to form an acid salt or soap with potassium hydroxide, evidencing the association of two molecules in this case.

Other factors that give evidence of the presence of double molecules in rosin are the iodine value and the speed of esterification. Though iodine values do not allow the drawing of quantitative conclusions as to the number of reactive points present in the molecule, they clearly indicate the degree of saturation. The iodine value of rosin, amounting only to the low value of 150, indicates considerable saturation of reactive points as is to be expected from the doubling up of single molecules. Such duplications create structural hindrances in the molecule of commercial rosin, which impede the esterification. Actual determinations show that the

speed of esterification

of rosin is considerably slower than that of monomeric monobasic acids, such as fatty acids. For example, samples of rosin and linseed oil fatty acids were heated at 260° C. with 10% glycerine under otherwise identical conditions, and the acid values were taken after 30 and 60 minutes respectively. After 30 minutes, only 20% of the rosin, but 65% of the linseed oil fatty acid were esterified; after 60 minutes the two figures were 35% and 75%.

There is no doubt that the doubling up of single molecules in rosin inactivates some of its reactive points. But manifold reactivities remain, as manifested by acid, saponification, acetyl values and chemical activities.

The acid value of rosin, being about 165, indicates the presence of slightly more than 10% of neutral bodies. The value decreases considerably on heating at temperatures of 275° C. or at higher temperatures. Six hours of heating at 275° C., for instance, reduces the acid value to 120. The decrease in acid value from about 165 to about 120 is accompanied by an increase in the content of

unsaponifiable matter.

For instance, while heating a rosin sample containing 5% unsaponifiable matter for 16 hours under vacuum at 275° C., the percentage of unsaponifiable material increased to 25%.

The saponification value of rosin is about 10 points higher than the acid value, if the orthodox method of saponification by alcoholic potassium hydroxide is applied, indicating the presence of about 5% of easily saponifiable esterlike substances. If the determination is carried out in higher boiling solvents as, for instance, butanol, higher values are obtained, evidencing the presence of esters or possibly lactones, which are difficult to saponify. There is no sharp dividing line between ester-like substances and unsaponifiable matter present in rosin.

Rosin possesses a very pronounced acetyl value, which may be found as high as 80. Only a small part of this value, however, is due to the presence of hydroxyl groups; the major part originates from the reaction of the acetic anhydride with the carboxyl groups of the rosin, forming simple or mixed acid anhydrides.

Rosin acids, at the high temperatures of resin manufacture, have a tendency to form acid anhydrides by the linking up of two molecules, accompanied by the elimination of water. The

residual acidity

of many rosin esters, or rosin-based synthetic resins, is due to such anhydrides, and not caused by actual carboxyl groups. Groups of anhydrides or mixed acid anhydrides do not react with alkali in the absence of water, and show acid reaction only after they have been converted into carboxyl groups by taking up water. This interesting fact is evidenced by the following simple experiment. The acid value of a commercial ester gum was determined in two different ways, one method dissolving the ester gum in a mixture of one part of toluol and two parts of 95% alcohol, and titrating with aqueous potassium hydroxide, the other method carefully excluding every trace of water, applying only completely dehydrated solvents and reagents. The first determination yielded an acid value of 12; the second one showed a figure of less than 0.5. The same results were obtained, using various types of indicators in the titration.

Other chemical reactivities of rosin are due to reaction capable points in the abietic structure itself which, due to its more than 20 carbon atoms, and its many branches and ramifications, offers ample opportunities to form linkages of different types, location and stability.

It is customary to explain the internal

structure of esterified rosin

by simple formulae. For instance, in the case of commercial ester gum, it is assumed that three abietic radicals are attached to one glycerine radical, or in the case of pentaerythritol resins, it is assumed that four abietic radicals are grouped around one pentaerythritol radical. It is surprising to note how such traditional conceptions, without any experimental background, have been carried through the literature for decades.

The determination of the molecular weights of rosin esters shows clearly that such formulae in no way represent the actual molecular configuration. The glycerol triabietate, as used for the orthodox formula, has a theoretical weight of about 950, compared to an actual molecular weight of about 800, determined for commercial ester gum. The pentaerythritol tetraabietate, as represented in the traditional formula, has a theoretical weight of about 1275, compared to an actual molecular weight of 1000, determined for commercial pentaerythritol ester resin. In these, as in other similar cases, the actual molecular weights are only about 80% of the theoretical values.

The reason for the surprisingly low molecular weights lies in the presence of

low molecular hydroxy esters

which are formed during the esterification process. In order to produce practically neutral rosin esters, it is necessary to use, in actual production, about the theoretical amount of esterifying alcohol, or a slightly higher quantity than that required to saturate the free acidity of the rosin present at the start of the process. During the procedure of esterification, the rosin is heated for a long period of time to temperatures at which decarboxylation takes place, evidenced by a strong decline in acidity. Esterification being a slow process, substantial amounts of rosin remain unesterified for a considerable length of time, and are exposed to decarboxylation.

The effect is that the amount of esterifying alcohol, originally equivalent to the initial rosin acidity, finally is present in considerable excess. The excess produces esters, in which part of the hydroxyl groups are not neutralized, and which have considerably lower molecular weights than the completely neutralized esters. To cite a few examples, an abietic glyceride, in which only two hydroxyl groups of the total of three are saturated has a molecular weight of 675, or an abietic pentaerythritol ester, in which only three hydroxyl groups of the available four are saturated, has a weight of 1000. Evaluating such figures in detail, it becomes clear that commercial rosins esters are mixtures of neutral ester resins with low molecular hydroxy esters, which still contain free hydroxyl groups. In the case of ester gum the molecular weight of 800 indicates that nearly 50% of the resinous material consists of the diabietate.

The low molecular weights of rosin esters exclude the

possibility of ether formation

which has often been discussed in the literature. Esterification would lead to a linkage of two molecules of glycerine diabietate, enlarging the molecule to a weight of more than 1300, which is never found.

Though molecular weights of rosin esters are lower than expected from theoretical considerations, their internal structure is decidedly complex and much more complicated than, for instance, the esters of long chain fatty acids, *i.e.* for example, drying oils. Taking the

speed of saponification

as a reasonable measure for the complexity of the internal structure of ester-like substances, the following two descriptive examples are given. Two samples, one a rosin glyceride, the other a varnish linseed oil, were refluxed with a solution of potassium hydroxide in butanol-toluol, applying double the amount of potassium hydroxide required for complete saponification. Under these conditions the linseed oil was saponified instantaneously, whereas the rosin glyceride was saponified to an extent of only 75%, even after one hour of refluxing.

The specific comments made with regard to glycerine and pentaerythritol esters also apply to other rosin esters of practical importance. These include the esters of the di-and tri-pentaerythritols, of manitol and sorbitol, of allyl- and poly-allyl alcohol, and of the trimethylol propane.

The build-up of rosin esters enters into all considerations of the internal structure of rosin-modified maleic resins, copal-type synthetics, and of rosin-modified phenolics, the last named class largely influenced by the structure of certain pure phenol resins.

The structure of pure phenol resins of the heat-setting, molding type, is of a highly complex nature, because a large number of individual phenol formaldehyde units are combined into one resin molecule, and several different types of reactive points are active in the agglomeration. The

structure of the pure phenolics

discussed in this book, *i.e.* of the oil-soluble resins, which are either permanently fusible or only mildly heat hardening, is of a considerably simpler nature, because only a few individual units and merely two different types of reactive points are involved.

To convey an idea of the structural build-up of the last named pure phenol resins, the cases of the formaldehyde condensates of the para tertiary butyl phenol and of the so-called bis phenol are discussed. The para tertiary butyl phenol is condensed with formaldehyde either by an acidic or by an alkaline catalyst, the bis phenol usually is combined with formaldehyde only by way of alkali condensation. In all cases liquid condensation products are obtained, which contain two different types of hydroxyls, *i.e.* both phenolic and alcoholic hydroxyl groups. During the resinification of the liquid condensation products, the two classes of hydroxyl groups enter into a reaction, which takes place either between the same sort of hydroxyl groups, or between phenolic and alcoholic hydroxyls, and thereby effect the bond between the individual molecular units, building up the larger aggregates.

The structural

changes during resinification

were investigated by exact determination of the increase in molecular weights, and of the decrease in the quantity of free phenolic and alcoholic hydroxyl groups, according to methods described in a later chapter. An interesting picture of the internal resin structure was obtained.

It was found that in general only about five individual molecules of the phenol-formaldehyde condensate were agglomerated into one resin molecule, that six monomeric units was the upper limit of association for acid-condensed resins, and eight monomolecular units the upper limit of agglomeration for alkli-condensed resins.

The acid-catalyzed phenol-formaldehyde condensate did did not lose any alcoholic hydroxyl groups during the resinification, which could have been expected from a possible internal linkage. While in the process of resinifying, this condensate, however, lost three-quarters of its free phenolic hydroxyl groups. This observation proved conclusively that the resin forming linkage between the individual units is entirely due to the interaction of the phenolic groups only. It is reasonable to assume that this

unusually simple type of bond

leads to a comparatively plain resin structure, which in turn explains the friable and unelastic properties of this resin type.

The alkali-catalyzed formaldehyde condensates showed an entirely different behavior when resinified by heat. On resinification they suffered a considerable loss in the quantity of both free phenolic and alcoholic hydroxyl groups, the number of free phenolic hydroxyls decreasing by three-quarters, and that of free alcoholic hydroxyls declining by one-quarter. Accordingly, both hydroxyl types took part in the resin forming reaction, and resinification occurred through the linkage of the two different classes of hydroxyl groups.

Being of a different chemical character, phenolic and alcoholic hydroxyl groups act differently in the molecular build-up of the resins. They probably lie in different planes, act in different directions and, therefore, are capable and eager to produce

three-dimensional structures.

This conception is in accordance with the physical properties of the alkali-condensed resins and their effect of mechanically hardening and strengthening other resins.

The three-dimensional structures formed by alkali-condensed formaldehyde condensates of para tertiary alkyl phenols and of bis phenol is the base for the internal structure of the majority of rosin-modified phenolics. As demonstrated by experiment in a later chapter, the alkali-catalyzed condensates do not enter into any chemical reaction with the rosin in the process of producing rosin-modified phenol resins. Inasmuch as no chemical linkage occurs, the process consists simply of a resinification of the pure phenolic condensate in the manner and to the degree previously described. In view of the fact that the condensate is present in more or less strongly diluted condition, the resinification does not lead to a highly knit phenolic resin structure, but to a loosely built three-dimensional lattice, like a honey comb structure.

According to this conception the

structure of modified phenolics

is a two-phase system of a framework of pure phenol resin with the cavities filled in by the rosin component. The phenolic framework is highly elastic, as evidenced by the peculiar mechanical properties of a modified phenolic when drawn into a thread. In this form it is elastic like a spring of steel. Elastic characteristics are definitely missing in the friable ester gum, which does not have the reinforcing network of a springy phenolic resin.

A recent development has produced alkali-condensed alkyl phenol-formaldehyde condensates of an etherlike character, in which one glycerine hydroxyl group per ether complex is left free for reaction with rosin. Using such compounds for the making of rosin-modified phenol resins, it is possible to produce a chemical link between the phenol formaldehyde condensates and the rosin component, which normally does not exist. The higher molecular complexity of the internal structure of such resins, improves their characteristics in protective coatings.

The molecular size of rosin-modified phenolics is comparatively small, characterizing them clearly as low molecular polymers. The molecular weight of commercial resins varies between 1200 and 1400. A technically important method is available to enlarge the molecular build-up by 50%, which is discussed in the chapter on maturing.

The internal structure of

rosin-modified maleic resins

is governed by rules of structural chemistry, which are very similar to those developed for phthalic anhydride resins. According to the structural rules governing alkyd resins, monobasic alcohols and acids not only do not contribute to resin formation, but delay or prevent it. Neither are dibasic acids or dihydric alcohols, when reacted together, capable of giving rise to resinous substances. The rules state that in order to form resins, it is necessary that one of the reacting alcohols or acids is at least dibasic and the other one is at least tribasic, or, speaking more generally, that one of the two reagents has at least two reactive points, and the other one at least three such points. Not only hydroxyl or carboxyl groups, but also double bonds, as are present in maleic acid, may serve as reactive points. Resin formation is also assured, if both of the reagents have three or more reactive points.

Resins formed by the 2-3, 3-2, 4-2, 3-3 or higher functional reactions are of the heat convertible type, which are capable of gelatinizing in the kettle by prolonged heating and which form insoluble films when baked.

Elaborate theories

have been developed to elucidate the relationship between the phenomenon of gelatinization and the structure of the resins. It is assumed that it is closely connected with the size, shape and weight of the molecules, which act as structural members of the resin structure, and that it is largely dependent on the way these structural members are assembled in the general construction. According to these conceptions, chainlike molecules produce soft, flexible resins. By branching of the chains and ring formation the resins become more rigid and the more so, the more reactive points take part in this reaction. By crosslinking of the chains, so to speak, through forming a structure of bonded brickwork pattern due to forces which act in three different directions, the resins acquire the property of gelatinizing into hard, viscous, insoluble, and infusible substances.

The structural conceptions previously described apply to resins in which the components are present in molecular ratios. They have to be modified if other ratios prevail, as is often the case in manufacturing procedures, or, if monobasic acids are present, which delay resin formation and prevent gelatinization.

Structural conceptions developed for alkyd resins apply, with slight modification, to rosin modified maleic resins. As a monobasic acid, which prevents gelatinization, rosin in its various forms is introduced, *i.e.* as gum rosin, wood rosin or polymerized rosin. As polyhydric alcohols, the dihydric diethylene glycol, the trihydric glycerine, the tetrahydric pentaerythritol and other poly-reactive alcohols may enter into the resin structure.

The polybasic acids entering the resin structure are, as a rule, not the maleic acid-type substances as such, *i.e.* not the maleic anhydride, the maleic acid, the fumaric acid or the malic acid themselves. Due to the strong tendency of these chemicals to link up with rosin, they immediately form

rosin-maleic type acids,

in practically all cases of resin production, before they start any other reactions. Therefore, the polybasic acids, which actually enter into the maleic resin structure, are either the rosin-maleic acid or the rosin-fumaric acid.

The rosin-maleic acid is usually obtained by reacting three parts of rosin with one part of maleic anhydride. It is a uniform chemical compound, which contains the two components in the ratio of their molecular weights and in the form of partially double molecules. During its formation it loses one of the three carboxyl groups which are initially present. By crystallization from ethyl alcohol, the rosin-maleic acid can be prepared in the monomeric crystalline form, which possesses an acid value of 280 and a molecular weight of 400. These figures prove that the rosin-maleic acid is dibasic.

The same type of dibasic acid is formed when rosin reacts with maleic acid and, to a certain extent, when rosin reacts with malic acid.

Fumaric acid links up with rosin in a structurally different manner. None of the carboxyl groups present in the two reactants is eliminated during the reaction, with the result that the

rosin-fumaric acid

is tribasic. This characteristic manifests itself in the properties of the finished resins. Rosin-fumaric acid favors three-dimensional structures more than rosin-maleic acid, and consequently fumaric resins have higher melting points and viscosities than maleic resins.

During the process of maleic resin-making, continuous inter-molecular exchanges take place between the components. This interchange is so pronounced that normally the resin properties are not influenced by the sequence in which the various components are combined. The mixed esters obtained usually have a molecular size of 1200 to 1400, which can be enlarged to one-and-a-half of this size by means of the maturing procedure.

A comparison of maleic and fumaric resins shows that resin properties depend not only on molecular size, but also on

the shape of the molecules.

Rosin-maleic acid, with its two carboxyl groups which act in only two directions, gives softer and thinner resins than rosin-fumaric acid, which has the same molecular weight, but possesses three carboxyl groups, capable of acting in three different directions. A systematic survey brings out the fact that two dimensional straight chain structures can be built up to a much higher molecular weight than three-dimensional cross-linked chain structures, until they become insoluble and infusible. An instructive example is the case of the two dimensional glycol succinate structure, which can be agglomerated to molecular weights of 3000 without losing fusibility and solubility, whereas the molecular weight of three-dimensional structures, such as that of most coating and ink resins, cannot be enlarged substantially beyond 2000 without the resins gelatinizing into an insoluble mass.

The ideas developed with regard to the relationship of resin properties and their molecular size and shape, contribute to an understanding of the

internal structure of copal-type synthetic resins.

The molecular weight of copal-type synthetics varies between 1700 and 1900, and is not essentially different from that of matured phenolic and maleic resins, but the shape of their molecular structure deviates considerably from that of the resin types named.

The different molecular form of the copal-type synthetics is due to the method of their production. Phenolic and maleic resins are made by a process of molecular build-up through polymerization and condensation of low molecular units into larger aggregates, whereas copal-type synthetics are produced by a molecular breakdown through degradation of high molecular materials, *i.e.* gelatinous resins are degelled and liquefied by means of heat and mechanical force. The resin gels used for this purpose are usually produced by overloading a rosin base with phenol-formaldehyde condensates, maleic-type compounds, polyhydric alcohols or solubilized natural copals and adjusting the relative amounts of ingredients, so that reversible gels and not infusible masses are formed.

During the

process of degelling

the three-dimensional gelatinous structure is partially broken up into two-dimensional molecular chains and, judging from the high solubility and fusibility of copal-type synthetics compared to other resin classes, the percentage of the last named structures must be high.

The internal structure of copal-type synthetics is distinguished by two other characteristics. While the large over-polymerized parts are reduced in size, the smaller units are enlarged during the production process, with the result that the resin molecules in the final product are of extremely uniform size. Copal-type synthetics are furthermore distinguished by free hydroxyl groups, which are present in the structure, probably in the form of partially alcoholized resin esters. They originate from an excess of polyhydric alcohol which is necessary for the depolymerization procedure. The presence of free hydroxyl groups constitutes

an interesting analogy

to the structure of natural copals, which also contain hydroxyl groups in the form of hydroxy esters and hydroxy acids.

For certain purposes, natural copals are introduced, in solubilized form, into copal-type synthetics. During the process of this combination, the great multitude of reactive points creates resin structures of especially high rigidity, according to the structural rules developed for alkyd resins, and extending such rules beyond normal polybasic acids and alcohols to apply to hydroxy acids and hydroxy esters.

VIEWS ON MOLECULAR WEIGHTS

As appears from the foregoing comments on the structure of phenolics, maleics and copal-type synthetics, all of these coating and ink resins have molecular weights which are considerably lower than those generally assumed in the literature. Contrary to the usual conception they are decidedly low polymers, with molecular weights rarely exceeding 2000, and not high polymers in the customary meaning of the word, *i.e.* implying molecular weights of at least several thousands. Even gelation of the resins, here under consideration, does not lead to the formation of particularly large molecules.

Several methods are available for the

determination of molecular weights

of the resins under consideration. Methods, based on osmotic conditions in solutions, are in successful use for high polymers, but are not suitable and adaptable for the determination of the molecular size of coating and ink resins. The measurement of viscosities of resin solutions under specified conditions, which is a useful method for high polymers, yields only rough estimates for coating and ink resins. Another suggested method consists in measuring the degree of solubility of resins and comparing solubility values with those obtained from resins with an established molecular weight. To determine the degree of solubility, a weighed amount of resin is dissolved in a solvent and a non-solvent is added until precipitation occurs or, the resin is dispersed in a non-solvent by heating until the solution becomes clear, and the temperature is observed at which clouding and precipitation occur on cooling.

Solubility methods do not give reliable results because they are based on the assumption that solubility decreases with an increase in molecular weight, which in no way is true for coating and ink resins. They furthermore do not take into consideration the fact that all normal resins contain molecular components of different weights, varying from low molecular parts to highly overpolymerized particles and, therefore, the values obtained depend largely on the amount of overpolymerized parts present, which are precipitated first, and are hardly influenced by portions of small molecular size.

Inasmuch as the previously named methods proved unsuitable for the correct determination of molecular weights of coating and ink resins, the classical methods of boiling point elevation and freezing point depression were investigated in detail. For the boiling point methods, ethylene dibromide was used, with 10% resin added to the solvent. Great care was required to secure constant temperatures, particularly in the elimination of drafts. In spite of all precautions, the accuracy of the readings was not greater than 0.1° to 0.2° C. For the freezing point method, camphor or diphenylamine was used. 10% resin was dissolved by gentle heating and the mixture was then allowed to cool very slowly. Outside influences again were difficult to eliminate and the accuracy of the readings was limited to one-fourth of one degree C. or less.

In both boiling and freezing point methods, the same order of magnitude was found for the molecular size, regardless of the type of solvent used. Obtaining similar values in ethylene dibromide, camphor or diphenylamine justifies the conclusion that identical values would be found in media, which are used as solvents in the actual practice of manufacturing surface coating and printing ink resins, such as xylol, mineral spirits, turpentine or kerosene.

As previously mentioned, the measured amounts of elevation or depression as determined by the orthodox methods, vary within comparatively wide limits, in fact within 10-25% and, therefore, the degree of accuracy obtained is insufficient to establish the molecular weight as an accurate constant for resin specifications. Serious efforts have been made in the author's laboratories to develop a correct method yielding reproducible figures with an accuracy of at least 1-2%.

A perfect procedure was developed by returning to the original

Beckmann freezing point method,

modifying it by using amounts of substance one hundred times larger than customary, and excluding outside influences by a heatable outer oil bath. Details of the method are described in a later chapter. As solvent, diphenylamine was utilized, *i.e.* either the chemically pure grade with a depression constant of 86, or the so-called purified grade with a constant of 83.5.

Diphenylamine is very suitable for molecular weight determinations because it has an exceptionally high depression constant. It is particularly useful for molecular weight determinations of the resins, studied in this volume, because it dissolves those resins quickly and completely at the low temperature of its own melting point, or slightly above this point, in a manner and to an extent quite analogous to that experienced with the customary solvents used for coating and ink resins. Diphenylamine is chemically inert at temperatures under 70° C. with the resins themselves, and also with the materials used or formed in resin manufacture, *i.e.* particularly rosin and resinous acids. It does not even react with the highly active maleic anhydride at this temperature, as evidenced by the fact that the theoretical molecular weight of maleic anhydride is found when diphenylamine is used for the determination.

The relative depression is independent of the concentration of the resin in the diphenylamine up to a resin content of 15%. As a rule, 10% of the resin is dissolved but percentages of 5% and lower are also practical. Smaller additions are usually employed if low molecular weights are expected. The resins dissolve easily at temperatures between 60° and 70° C., *i.e.* about 10° C. above the melting point of the diphenylamine. After solution is complete, the mixture is allowed to cool slowly. The temperature drops considerably under the actual freezing point due to super-cooling. The drop stops suddenly, crystals appear through the mixture, and the temperature rises quickly to a high point, at which peak it remains constant for several minutes.

This point of constant temperature is the correct freezing point of the mixture. To establish the amount of depression, the freezing point of the pure diphenylamine has been determined previously in the same way. The method yields temperatures which are reproducible to one one-hundredth of a degree. Its accuracy is due to the large amount of material used, whereby outside influences are excluded, quite different from the traditional Beckmann method, in which only small weights of substances were used, and many disturbing factors were not reliably eliminated.

Routine determinations are carried out by repeating the melting and freezing several times. Findings are considered to be correct if the readings check within a fraction of one one-hundredth of a degree. Inasmuch as depressions vary generally between 0.5 to 1.5 degrees, the accuracy thus achieved is about 1%. This degree of preciseness makes the new method suitable for both technical and scientific purposes. Its results serve as the base for a number of new conceptions outlined in this volume.

The molecular weights of the various

types of rosin,

including commercial abietic acid, are much higher than generally assumed. The chemical formula of abietic type acids yields a molecular weight of about 300. This weight is only found in chemically pure abietic acid, but never in commercial rosin. A series of determinations shows that all types of rosin exceed the theoretical weight by more than 200 units, and further proves the surprising fact that all grades of rosin, *i.e.* pale and dark colored grades of both gum or wood rosin types are practically alike in molecular size, their weight varying between 520 and 540. This is also true for commercial abietic acid and even for hydrogenated rosin.

Commercial grades of polymerized rosin are only slightly larger in molecular size, their molecular weights varying from 625-650.

Rosin esters have higher molecular weights than the non-esterified rosin. They vary between 700 and 1000, depending upon whether ordinary rosin or polymerized rosin is esterified, upon their method of manufacture, upon the completeness of esterification and finally depending upon the type of esterifying alcohol used. Within the limits of 700 to 1000, the glycol esters have the lowest weight and pentaerythritol esters have the highest weight, with glycerine esters occupying a middle position. In all cases it is found that the molecular sizes are much smaller than calculated for a normal ester. Since the molecular weights do not even reach that of the theoretical compounds, there is no evidence whatsoever of the presence of large molecular aggregates formed by etherification.

The molecular weight of Congo copals depends entirely on the degree of their depolymerization. Before becoming oil-soluble in the gum running process, their molecular weight is higher than 2000. During the copal melting procedure the molecular weight decreases with the degree of degradation, reaching 1200 after a running loss of 25%, and finally decreasing to the level of ordinary rosin, *i.e.* about 600. This low level is reached after the copal has suffered a fusing loss of 50%.

The molecular weight which indicates the molecular

size of synthetic resins

varies among the different groups and within each class, depending on several factors, particularly on melting point, composition and treatment.

Pure phenolics, both the acid- and alkali-condensed types, have relatively low molecular weights, the degree of molecular association depending upon the temperature to which they have been heated for dehydration and hardening. Liquid or soft resins contain molecular aggregates of one to three single molecules, hard resins contain aggregates of four to eight single molecules. As a rule the molecular weight of commercial pure phenolics varies within the relatively narrow limits of 650 and 900.

Normal rosin-modified phenolics are of a molecular size in the order of 1200–1400. When subjected to the maturing process described in the next chapter, their size increases and their molecular weight may reach the level of 1800–2000. If their molecular size is enlarged by particularly high amounts of the phenol-formaldehyde component, or by the use of high molecular polyhydric alcohol, the size may exceed 2000, with the result that they become gelatinous and insoluble.

Orthodox rosin-modified maleics possess about the same molecular size as modified phenolics. Their molecular weight can be increased to values of 1800 to 2000 either by the maturing procedure, by the incorporation of large amounts of maleic type compounds or by overloading them with esterifying alcohols. If, due to an excessive amount of reactive materials, the molecular weight exceeds 2000, the resin starts to form gelatinous particles and finally becomes insoluble and gelatinizes throughout.

Copal-type synthetics may vary in molecular size within the molecular range of 1600 to 2000. Their weight, however, mostly remains within the limits of 1700 to 1900, in accordance with the degree of depolymerization to which they have been subjected in the process of manufacture.

As appears from the previous comments, the molecular weights of the rosin-based synthetics under consideration for the purpose of producing high-grade surface coatings and printing inks, fall within the range of 1200 and 2000. Molecular weights substantially lower or higher than these figures render the resins unsuitable for the purposes in question.

Molecular weights lower than 1200 are found in resinous esters which have low melting points and low viscosities. They are also found in resins which lack resistance against hydrolysis, oxidation and other weathering influences. Another drawback connected with small molecular sizes in resins, is the tendency to crystallize from solutions or in the film.

The interesting relationship between

crystallization tendency and molecular weight

can be studied by observing, under the microscope, the process of crystal formation of substances of known molecular weight and is shown by three photographs in *Figure 3*. They are

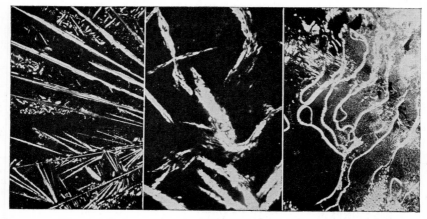

FIGURE 3.   Influence of molecular weight on crystallization.

taken with polarized light, because ordinary light is unsuitable for microscopic investigations of this type. Ordinary light shows crystals only after they are clearly formed, and then merely their outlines and not their internal structure. Polarized light, however, makes visible the very beginning of crystal formation, even when the crystals are still in the sub-semi-crystalline state. Polarized light has this ability because it does not penetrate through amorphous substances, and is transmitted only when the material is, or becomes, doubly refracting, due to internal orientation as, for instance, by crystallization. The amount of light transmitted depends upon the degree of orientation.

Using this optic principle, the three microphotographs of *Figure 3* were taken. They show the sodium soaps of caprylic, myristic and oleic acids, all three crystallizing under the same condition from an aqueous solution. Watching the process of

crystallization under the microscope

with polarized light, the field of observation first remains entirely dark, until the moment when crystalline orientation begins to develop. Caprylic acid, with a molecular weight of 144, shows very distinct needle-shaped crystals. Myristic acid with a molecular weight of 228, yields crystalline aggregates of fair degree of orientation. Oleic acid, with a molecular weight of 296, displays vague forms of only semicrystalline character. Soaps of higher molecular acids lose even the small power of orientation, shown by oleic acid. Sometimes such residual forces can be made visible by exerting a slight lateral pressure on the microscopic specimen by shifting the micro cover glass on top of the slide; under this influence the molecules orientate themselves into pseudocrystalline aggregates which light up under polarized light.

The upper limit of molecular size, beyond which the tendency for crystallization seems to vanish, is approaching the molecular weight of 700. As evidence, the tri-myristine can be considered, which has a weight of 724. It has no real tendency to crystallize any more, but still possesses sufficient power of orientation to form indistinctly defined crystals. The molecular weight of commercial ester gum comes close to this limit and resinous products of this type, therefore, may cause difficulties through their tendency to separate crystalline matter.

The molecular sizes of high-class coating and ink resins are sufficiently above the upper limit of the molecular size mentioned before to protect them against the

danger of crystallization.

Such dangers are twofold. First, resins with an inclination to crystal formation impair the can stability of surface coating and printing ink materials containing them. On long storage, especially at low temperature, they tend to precipitate crystalline matter from varnishes, enamels, inks or lacquers. Second, such resins reduce the durability of the dried surface coating films containing them. They are prone to form crystals in the coating, and any such crystal will act as a foreign matter, disrupting the homogeneity of the film and functioning as starting point for the breakdown of the surface coating. Even if distinct crystals are not developed, the internal tension, which precedes the act of crystallization, considerably weakens the film.

Molecular weights exceeding 2000 render the resins impractical for coating and ink purposes. Fusibility, solubility and viscosity change to an extent that the resins become too difficult to melt in the varnish kettle, too difficult to dissolve in the oils and solvents used in the coating and ink industries, and too viscous in solution for practical handling. The value of 2000 seems low in view of the fact that other polymers, like those of glycol succinates, with molecular weights of more than 3000, remain soluble and fusible. The reason is to be found in the more

complex internal structure

of coating and ink resins, which probably is of a three-dimensional nature.

Questions of molecular weights of resins have not received the attention due them in the coating and ink field. Such questions have been considered as purely theoretical, or at least highly controversial. The previous comments, based on accurate experiments, clearly show the great practical importance of the molecular weight of resins in connection with their manufacture and application. The comments also point the way to a highly interesting new field of research and development.

THE MATURING PROCESS

The usefulness of rosin-modified phenol and maleic resins can be improved for surface coatings and inks by a newly developed process, by which their molecular size can be considerably enlarged. As pointed out in a previous chapter, the normal commercial resins of this type possess relatively small molecular sizes, *i.e.* molecular weights of only 1200–1400. When their molecular size is enlarged, they gain considerably in hardness, solubility, chemical resistance and heat stability.

There are several methods available to achieve this result. The usual method consists in increasing the amounts of phenol-formaldehyde condensates, maleic acid-type compounds, or polyhydric alcohols to be combined with the rosin element in the resin. However, both such processes and products have very definite disadvantages. For mass production purposes the procedure is not practical, because gelatinization may occur at an early moment, stopping the agitator, causing exothermic reactions and possibly overfoaming or fire. The products, due to the excessive amount of expensive additions, are high in cost, they possess low solubility, which is a distinct technical disadvantage, and contain large percentages of overpolymerized resin particles, which makes them inhomogeneous and incompatible with many oils and pigments.

An improved method of obtaining large molecular resinous esters of outstanding characteristics is used to produce the copal-type synthetic resins previously discussed, and consists in the application of high heat, substantially above the temperature of normal resin formation, whereby the excessively agglomerated oversize molecules with weights higher than 2000 are reduced to a molecular size of 1700–1900.

Quite different from this way of working, the

newly developed method

creates large molecular resinous esters with molecular weights of 1800 to 2000 by building them up from the usual small sized molecules with molecular weights of 1200–1400. To achieve this purpose, the resins which have been produced in the orthodox cycle of resin manufacture, are subjected to a vacuum treatment at a temperature which is kept substantially lower than the temperature of normal resin formation.

This process can fittingly be called maturing, because it brings about a molecular change, which is similar to that which occurs during the old method of maturing fossil gum varnishes by storing them, at constant and slightly elevated temperature, for periods of 12–24 months. During the maturing period a molecular agglomeration within the varnish took place, which greatly improved its technical properties. The reaction speed of molecular changes is counted in months at the low temperature of varnish storage tanks, whereas it is figured in hours at the high temperature of the resin kettles.

Agglomeration of molecules during resin maturing is based on both polymerization, which proceeds without the elimination of water, and condensation, which is accompanied by the splitting off of water. Agglomeration is facilitated by the application of vacuum and is promoted by the presence of phenolic- or maleic-type substances. The length of time required for the maturing process depends on the

increase of molecular weight

desired; it varies with the chemical composition of the resin, and the conditions of temperature and vacuum. As a rule, the time should be not less than 16 hours and not more than 24 hours, meaning that in actual practice occasionally a full day and night has to be added to the orthodox production cycle. The speed of molecular aggregation slows down generally after 18 hours of treatment and becomes negligible after 24 hours.

The maturing process is based on painstaking requirements and controls with regard to time, temperature and vacuum; and, therefore, requires carefully designed machinery and equipment. Electrical heat is particularly suitable for this purpose, because it allows exceedingly exact temperature control over unusually long periods of time. Molecular enlargement or maturing effects cannot be attained, for obvious reasons, by processing resins in open, movable varnish kettles.

Rosin-modified phenolic and maleic resins with melting points of 130–170° C., and molecular weights of 1200 to 1400 are the type of resins susceptible to the maturing process, whereby their molecular weights are increased to the range of 1850 to 1950. Molecular weights attainable in the maturing process do not exceed 2000 because, in order to reach higher sizes, the resins must be of the gelation capable type, whereas the process is applied only to compositions which will not gelatinize on continuous heating.

Maturing improves hardness, solubility, chemical resistance and heat resistance through a new procedure. So far, it has been the unwritten rule in resin production that compromises must be made to produce extraordinary constants in one and the same resin, *i.e.* that one outstanding characteristic must be sacrificed for another important characteristic; for instance, if great hardness was produced, the solubility was reduced or, if high solubility was created, the chemical resistance might be at a low point.

The maturing procedure now makes it possible to improve several resin properties at the same time

without making such compromises.

For instance, the hardness improves markedly, whereas the viscosity barely changes, an observation which is quite contrary to the usual experience. Furthermore, in spite of increased hardness, the solubility is improved, which reverses an old established rule of resin technology, according to which solubility decreases with increasing hardness. Another unusual feature is the balancing of the two opposite features of chemical resistance and solubility during the maturing process, in which the molecular agglomeration produces higher chemical resistance, together with higher solubility in complete parallelism.

The hardness of matured resins, as measured by the melting point, is improved by 10-20° C. which has a very beneficial effect on the bodying and drying characteristics of the resins.

Solubility values increase decidedly during maturing. In the case of maleics, this increase is so intense that the entire character of the resin is changed. This change can be demonstrated by titrating a resin solution in a strong solvent with a weak solvent, until an incipient cloud appears.

At this time it should be mentioned that, in determining solubility by titration, the highly polymerized parts of the resin, which are present in every normally produced resin, are precipitated first and that, therefore, increased titration values are evidence of a decrease in the amount of high molecular particles. Since maturing otherwise is based on a molecular build-up of the low molecular parts, as previously pointed out, the process effects a thorough homogenization of the resin by equalizing the molecular sizes of the various resin portions. The removal of highly polymerized matter improves the pigment stability of the resins, because the surface activity of many pigments causes high molecular resin particles to gelatinize, when they come into contact with each other in paints and enamels.

The chemical resistance increases with the molecular size

because the resinous molecules aggregate at double bonds or other reactive points, which are easily attacked by outside influences, but which are eliminated by the process of agglomeration. This process is quite analogous to the formation of highly viscous bodied oils, the resistance of which improves during the bodying period, due to inter-molecular linkages. The

disappearance of weak spots

in the resin molecule is indicated by the decided drop of the iodine value during the maturing process.

The decrease of the iodine absorption values during maturing of resins is more pronounced for modified phenolics than for maleics. In the case of maleic resins, fewer reactive points are available at the beginning, because open places in the rosin molecule have been closed through reaction with the maleic radical. The difference in iodine values of phenolics and maleics might also be due to the fact that in the case of phenolics, additional reactive points disappear, because the maturing of modified phenolics is accompanied by an agglomeration of the phenolic component, which initially may have consisted of 5 units and which may grow into aggregations of 8 units.

The increase in chemical resistance of matured resins is also indicated by the distinct slowdown in the speed with which the resins are saponified, saponification speeds actually declining 20-25% due to maturing. Water and alkali resistance in turn are improved accordingly.

For the determination of the

speed of saponification

a special method must be applied because, in the usual procedure, the resins are not properly saponified. In this method 10 grams of resin are dissolved in toluol, the solution is filled up with toluol to 100 c.c. and 50 c.c. of a $1N$ solution of potassium hydroxide in butanol are added. The saponification mixture is then boiled under reflux, and samples of 15 c.c. each are taken for back titration every hour. Constant values indicate completion of the saponification. For this purpose the ester values are used, obtained by deducting the respective acid values from the saponification numbers. The speed of saponification is indicated by the percentage of the ester value, determined after a certain specified time, with reference to the total ester value.

The molecular enlargement, as it manifests itself in the resins by their improved chemical resistance, has a beneficial effect on the durability of the resin oil film. On the other hand, it must be kept in mind that the molecular enlargement, as promoted by maturing, will also reduce the degree of chemical reactivity with oils in varnish cooking, and may, if carried too far, lead to completely inert and inactive resins.

Acid values of resins subjected to maturing must not be too high and should be within the range customary for esterified products, that is to say, generally between 25 and 50. During the molecular aggregation, acid values decline steadily, mainly due to the application of vacuum, which continuously removes volatile acids. The chemical resistance increases simultaneously, because it is the presence of such acids which makes the resins vulnerable to attacks by alkali. The

acidity decreases

to about half of its initial value in maleics, and can be brought down close to neutrality in modified phenolics, allowing for the acidity, which is due to the presence of free phenolic hydroxyl groups. As demonstrated elsewhere, phenolic hydroxyl groups act as carboxyl groups in the method of acid value determination.

Whereas acidity decreases, the total saponification values remain unchanged during the molecular enlargement, evidencing the fact that no unsaponifiable matter is formed. Therefore, the decline in acid values during maturing must not be confused with the decrease of acidity undergone by free rosin on heating at temperatures higher than 270° C. Quite different from the maturing of resins, the cracking of rosin lowers its melting point by 20 to 30° C., and produces high percentages of unsaponifiable matter, *i.e.* 25% or more, proving that decarboxylation, with the formation of hydrocarbon-like substances, takes place.

It lies in the nature of the maturing process, which applies vacuum for a long period of time, that it reduces the loss which resins undergo on further heating in the varnish kettle, with or without other resins or oils, *i.e.* improves their heat stability. Experience shows that matured resins have two or three times the heat stability of non-matured material. The heat loss is determined by weighing before and after heating 300 grams of resin in a 600 c.c. beaker for one hour at 285° C.

The previous comments on the possibilities of enlarging the molecular sizes of certain coating and ink resins and thereby improving their technical properties, are explained further in the later chapters on phenol and maleic resins, in which highly interesting specific cases are discussed in detail.

Research on maturing, as well as on other fundamental resin problems, is carried out in a

laboratory research assembly

of the type pictured in *Figure 4*. This picture, as well as other colored prints in this volume, are produced by four color printing from plates, which are based on kodachrome transparencies. Such transparencies are made on color film, using a standard studio camera of 8 x 10-inch size, equipped with a color-corrected lens, together with the proper type of filter. As light source powerful photo flood lights of 500-750 watt intensity are used. In order to bring out the true color value, exposure times have to be carefully studied with the help of a master exposure meter, because of the limited latitude of color films.

Starting a detailed description of the picture of the laboratory resin making apparatus, there is visible on the right hand side the rheostat, by which the electrical current used for heating the reaction vessel is regulated. The rheostat is a variable audio transformer which controls the voltage, and is not a resistance instrument. Next to the rheostat a flowmeter, calibrated in millimeters, is visible. It measures the flow of the inert gas, particularly of the carbon dioxide used in the processes, which is obtained from a cylinder and is led into the reaction vessel through a separate valve and delivery tube, to be seen on the left hand side of the flowmeter.

The reaction still is a three neck balloon or boiling flask with ground glass joints, equipped with a direct-driven agitator. The agitator shaft goes through a vacuum and pressure-tight stainless steel stuffing box, and carries a foambeater, an impeller and a propeller, all made of stainless steel. Additional equipment of the reaction flask consists of ground glass joint thermometers, graduated from 0-360° C., and a feeding funnel as reservoir for liquid additions, equipped with adapter tubes and flow regulating valves.

An essential feature of the resin vessel is a reflux condenser column, which can be cooled by either water or refrigerating liquid; it can be closed off in case vacuum or pressure is applied. The apparatus shown in the picture is not usually used for pressure operations, but can be adapted to it with minor changes. The top of the reflux condenser is equipped with an adaptor for a thermometer and a delivery tube for volatile gases. The latter leads into the receptacle, which is designed for receiving decomposition and by-products.

The electric motor, which drives the agitator, is of a type built especially for this purpose. It is equipped with a reduction gear and an electrically controlled governor to keep a constant speed, even with widely varying resistance to agitation. The speed can be set at any rate that may be desired.

FIGURE 4. Laboratory apparatus used in resin research.

The heating furnace used in this laboratory unit is built on the basis of years of

experience in electrical heating.

It is most satisfactory, because it allows complete heat control and yields heating conditions which come very close to those in actual production units. The furnace uses Nichrome resistance wires, which are embedded in a special type of refractive material, in a way that they do not come into direct contact with the flask and that no hot spots can develop.

The outlet of the reaction vessel consists of a wide tube, provided with a two-way stopcock, which leads either into the vacuum receiver or into the by-product receptacle.

The vacuum receiver is a three neck ground glass joint balloon flask. One neck is connected through an adaptor with the reaction flask. The center opening is fitted directly to a mercury manometer. The third neck carries an adaptor containing a stopcock, which permits the drawing off of vapors by means of the vacuum pump, either directly or by way of an intermediate condenser. The latter, designed for reflux purposes, can be cooled either by air, water or refrigeration, and carries at its upper end a special type thermometer and a valve or stopcock, which leads directly to the vacuum pump.

The fume or by-product receiver, visible on the left side of the picture, is connected with the reaction vessel by a fume condenser, which precipitates the volatile material leaving the resin still. It applies water cooling, or uses artificially cooled liquids in the event that very volatile substances are to be condensed. The fume receiver itself is a balloon flask with one outlet leading out to the atmosphere outside the building and two inlets for pipes, one coming from the top of the reaction flask condenser and one from the reaction vessel directly.

The vacuum pump at the extreme left of the illustration is a motor driven, rotary-type pump, which is completely im-

mersed in high vacuum sealing oil. The pump produces a
vacuum of up to 29 inches, which is required during the resin
research operations.

The salient point in the

design of all laboratory equipment

for research on resin production, is to approach large scale
conditions as closely as possible. The above described laboratory apparatus fulfills this requirement, because it allows perfect reproduction of the heating cycle used in the plant, and
approaches closely the effects of agitation and vacuum in production kettles. The last two factors are much more difficult
to adjust in laboratory apparatus than are the conditions of
time and temperature.

REACTIVITIES BETWEEN RESINS AND OILS

It is the object of varnish making to produce completely
homogeneous combinations of resins with vegetable oils of the
oxidizing type. Inasmuch as both resins and oils are active
components in varnish-making procedures, the properties and
reactivities of both are important.

The reactivities of drying oils with resins depend on their
state of polymerization and degree of saturation. As a rule,
the reactivity of bodied oils is lowered, because polymerization
links up the individual molecules

through their reactive points,

thereby saturating and eliminating the active points which
have the ability to link up with resins. For instance, dehydrated castor oil, which is highly resin-reactive when unbodied, loses much of its chemical reactivity with resins as a
result of polymerization.

Resin reactivities of oils decrease with their degree of saturation, according to the established rule, that reactions are the

more intense the larger the number of active points for possible activities. The chemical nature of such points varies, the most important ones being isolated or conjugated double bonds, the last named types showing particularly pronounced reaction capacity. As a rule, the activities of the oils increase in the following order: soya oil, fish oil, linseed oil, perilla oil, dehydrated castor oil, oiticica oil, China wood oil.

An important factor governing oil reactivities is the degree of stability with which the fatty acid radical is attached to the esterifying alcohol or, in other words,

the degree of mobility

which these radicals possess for interchange reactions with other fatty acids, polyhydric alcohols or esters of fatty acids. The mobility of the fatty acid and alcohol radicals in vegetable oils is surprisingly high, as it appears from many observations in varnish-making and laboratory practice.

Good evidence of mobility is the ease with which monoglycerides and diglycerides are formed, when glycerine is heated with linseed oil in the presence of a small amount of lead oxide as accelerator; or the great speed with which linseed oil can be converted into an alcohol-soluble hydroxy ester by heating with pentaerythritol in the presence of a small amount of calcium naphthenate as catalyst.

Another good evidence of mobility is the speed and completeness of interchange reactions, when two different fatty acid glycerides are heated together, leading to the formation of mixed esters. An example is the heat-bodying together of oleic glyceride and linoleic glyceride. Before heating, unchanged linolenic glyceride may be separated from such a mixture by precipitation as the hexabromide. After heating the two components together for two hours at 225° C., the two glycerides cannot again be separated by precipitation. Additions of bromine will no longer cause the formation of insoluble hexabromides, as it does with the linoleic glyceride, because the latter loses its identity due to an interaction between the two glycerides, forming a new, chemically homogenious, mixed ester.

Further evidence of the great mobility of the acid and alcoholic radicals present in oils is found in the reaction when linseed oil is

heated with calcium resinate.

Calcium resinate is particularly suitable for the study of interchange reactions of the fatty acid glyceride components because of the good mobility of its own components. The investigation of its reactivities with linseed oil is described in the following comments. Complete analytical details are given at the same time, because they well serve as a practical example of the quantitative analysis of resin oil combinations.

Equal amounts by weight of varnish-linseed oil and calcium resinate, containing 6% calcium oxide, having an acid value of 65, are fused together gently at 200° C., and a sample of this mixture is taken. The resinate-oil mixture is then heated to 280° C., and held for 10 hours at this temperature, using carbon dioxide to prevent oxidation, when a second sample is taken.

For both samples

an exact determination

is made of (1) the free resinous and fatty acids, (2) the acidic material combined with calcium, (3) the unsaponifiable matter, (4) the saponifiable glycerine esters.

To determine the

free acids,

the sample is dissolved in petroleum ether, the same volume of 50% alcohol is added and the mixture titrated to neutrality with $1N$ alcoholic potassium hydroxide. The number of c.c.

of potassium hydroxide used indicates the acid value of the sample. The water-alcohol layer is drawn off and washed twice with petroleum ether. The combined petroleum ether portions in turn are washed with slightly alkaline 50% alcohol. The water-alcohol solution is concentrated on the water bath, until the alcohol is evaporated completely. The soaps present are split by weak hydrochloric acid and the free acids thereby liberated are extracted by ether. After the evaporation of the ether, they are weighed and identified.

To determine the acidic material which is

chemically combined with calcium,

the petroleum ether portions, obtained in the first step of the analysis, are shaken with the same volume of water, slowly adding $1N$ aqueous hydrochloric acid. The titration with acid is continued until methyl orange, used as an indicator, turns red. In this way, the calcium present in the sample is carried over into the aqueous layer and is eliminated.

The petroleum ether portion, after complete separation from the water layer, is mixed with the same volume of 50% alcohol and an amount of $1N$ potassium hydroxide is added, which is exactly equivalent to the amount of hydrochloric acid previously used. The water-alcohol layer is then separated from the petroleum ether layer, washed with petroleum ether as previously described, and concentrated on the water bath until the alcohol is evaporated. The residue is thinned with water, acidified with mineral acid, and extracted with ether. The ether extracts, after evaporation of the solvent, yield the acidic material, which is chemically combined with calcium. It can be weighed and identified.

To determine the

unsaponifiable matter

in the sample, the petroleum ether portions, determined in the second step of the analysis, are evaporated with an excess of alcoholic potassium hydroxide on the water bath, the residue is dissolved in alcohol, and the solution is refluxed for one hour to obtain complete saponification of all ester-like material. The liquid finally is concentrated to dryness on the water bath, the residue dissolved in 50% alcohol and, by repeated shaking with petroleum ether, the unsaponifiable matter is extracted. The extracts, on evaporation, yield the unsaponifiable matter, which can be weighed and identified.

To determine the

saponifiable glycerine esters

the aqueous-alcoholic portion remaining in the third step of the analysis, is acidified. The acids precipitated thereby are dissolved in ether and, finally, after evaporation of the ether, weighed and identified. They are the acids which, in the sample, are chemically combined with glycerine.

The results of the analysis of the two samples are reported in *Table 1.*

Table 1. Chemical Changes of Calcium Resinate-Oil Combination During Heating Period

Components Isolated and Identified	Sample Taken at 200° C.		Sample Taken After 10 Hours at 280° C.	
	Per-centage	Characteristics of Substance	Per-centage	Characteristics of Substance
Free acids	18%	Rosin-like, acid value 160	9%	Resinous material, acid value 260
Acidic material combined with calcium	26%	Rosin-like, acid value 160	24%	Fatty acid-like, acid value 195
Unsaponifiable matter	3%	Viscous oil	12%	Viscous oil
Acidic material combined with glycerine	44%	Fatty acid-like, acid value 190	46%	Resinous material, Lieberman-Storch positive

The sum total of free acids, acidic material combined with

calcium, unsaponifiable matter and acid substances, combined with glycerine, found in one hundred parts, is only about 90 parts for both samples, due to the separation and elimination of the calcium and glycerine radicals.

The free acids decrease during the ten-hour cooking period at 280° C. from 18% to 9%, *i.e.* to about the same extent as the unsaponifiable matter increases, which is from 3% to 12%, probably due to decarboxylation of free rosin present. The acidity of the free acids contained in the final sample, amounting to an acid value of 260, is one hundred units higher than the acidity initially present, possibly due to the formation of inner anhydrides or low molecular acids.

The occurrence of an

interchange reaction

can be derived from the data in *Table 1,* by comparing the quantity and characteristics of the acidic material combined with calcium to that of the acid substances which are chemically attached to the glycerine, making the comparison in both cases before and after the heating procedure. The percentages of the acidic materials do not change practically, but their properties undergo a very characteristic change. The acid bound originally to the calcium is rosin acid, but is found to be of fatty acid character after the heating period. The acid attached initially to the glycerine radical is linseed oil fatty acid, but is found after the cooking period to possess resinous character, showing a positive Lieberman-Storch reaction.

These observations indicate that rosin and fatty acids exchange their positions during the heating period, the rosin moving from the calcium to the glycerine, and the fatty acids migrating from the glycerine to the calcium.

Another evidence of the great mobility of the radicals in fatty acid esters, especially in linseed oil, is the ease with which fatty acids are esterified with glycerine and the high speed with which the fatty acid esters are saponified by means of free alkali.

In the process of combining oils and resins the

role played by the resins

is of the same importance as that of the oils. The type and degree of the resin activities vary with the individual resins, and several interesting rules can be established governing the chemical reactivities of coating and ink resins when in contact with oils.

The majority of the resins under consideration are rosin-based resinous esters which, in analogy to fatty esters, can be expected to enter into an ester interchange with oil on prolonged heating, in the way that part of the fatty acid radicals moves from the oily ester to the resinous ester and, vice versa, part of the resin acid radicals is transferred from the resin to the oil. Contrary to this expectation, however, rosin esters are very inert with oils and the mobility of their components is negligibly small compared to that of fatty acid esters.

The great difference in

mobility of the two ester types

of fatty and resinous esters is apparent from the following observations. Ester gum cannot be alcoholized by heating with glycerine, whereas oils are quickly converted into hydroxy esters on heating with glycerine. Rosin esters are extremely difficult to saponify; several hours of refluxing with an excess of alcoholic potassium hydroxide are required to effect complete saponification whereas, under the same saponifying conditions, a fatty acid ester is saponified instantaneously.

The difference in mobility of fatty and resinous radicals is also apparent from their behavior on esterification. Fatty acids are esterified much more quickly than rosin acids, all other conditions being equal. This fact is known from practical experiences in the varnish kettle, and also appears from the well established analytical method used to separate fatty acids and rosin. In this method, the mixture of fatty and rosin acids is dissolved in ten times its weight of absolute alcohol, and the solution is saturated with dry hydrochloric acid, maintaining room temperature through cooling. After one hour's standing, the fatty acid is completely esterified, whereas the rosin has remained unchanged.

Due to the

lack of mobility

in rosin esters, no exchange of acid and alcohol radicals takes place when a rosin ester is heated with a fatty acid ester, for instance, when ester gum is heat-bodied with linseed oil. The question is brought up eventually as to whether or not interchange reactions take place in rosin ester varnishes during storage. As is known, fossil gum varnishes are matured for twelve to eighteen months in storage tanks, and there is no doubt that during this period certain molecular rearrangements take place in the varnish solution, producing quicker drying, higher gloss and better durability of the varnish film. For rosin ester varnishes, however, no actual evidence has been found that reactions take place on storage which produce similar results.

According to the foregoing comments,

mixed esters of fatty and rosin esters

are not easily prepared. In order to produce them, it is necessary to alcoholize the oil first and then to react the hydroxy esters thus obtained with free rosin. This principle of producing mixed esters is not recommended for varnish making, because from a practical point of view, both the process and the product are unsatisfactory. For instance, applying this method to the combination of linseed oil, glycerine and rosin, possibly with the reinforcing addition of maleic anhydride, a mixed ester is obtained which is impractical because it bodies very slowly and possesses low water resistance. Through replacing the glycerine by pentaerythritol, mixed esters are obtained which are also impractical, because their bodying speed is too slow for most purposes and they show a tendency to form gelatinous particles.

The immobility of the resinous radical in rosin esters when heated with oils, and their inability to form orthodox mixed esters, is considerably more pronounced in the case of the coating and ink resins under consideration in this study, *i.e.* of modified phenolics, maleics and copal-type synthetics. All these resins are

elaborately processed resinous esters

in which the mobility of the acid and alcoholic components are inactivated much further than in ordinary rosin esters.

As a result, no mixed esters of the type previously discussed are formed on heating with oils, and no exchange of acidic or alcoholic radicals can be detected. Nevertheless, very pronounced reactions take place in the majority of resin oil cooks, but they are of an entirely different nature. They are based on the reactivity of either phenolic or alcoholic hydroxyls, or on the action of non-volatile carboxyl or anhydride groups, each of which reactive groups may be present in the resins either separately or collectively, as will be shown in later chapters.

Furthermore, certain phenolic hydroxyl groups are able to link up with neutral oils by entering the fatty acid chain. Although alcoholic hydroxyl groups are unable to combine with neutral oils, they have the ability of interacting with decomposition products of the oils, which are formed through the high heat of the varnish cooking process and which consist of free fatty acids and partially split glycerides. Such decomposition products are present, to a small extent, in many unbodied oils, their amount increasing with the bodying of the oils. They are formed continuously during the varnish-cooking procedure at a comparatively quick rate which amounts to the formation of several per cent of free carboxyl groups per hour at bodying temperatures of 580-600° F.

The chemistry of the

heat decomposition of oils

is involved, but the fact is established that acidic material is formed. It can be assumed that one portion of those acidic substances is free fatty acid and that another portion is acid glyceride originating from the polymerized oil, which usually consists of two to three individual oil molecules. Consequently, any material that reacts with the carboxyl groups of such acid glycerides as, for instance, resins containing alcoholic hydroxyls, enters into the oil molecule itself.

Carboxyl and anhydride groups are present in many resins in the form of acid anhydrides. Having been subjected to a long period of vacuum treatment under high temperature, these substances, firmly attached to the resin molecule, possess a high degree of heat stability and are practically non-volatile at varnish-making temperatures. When resins containing such acid anhydrides are heated with oils, the fatty acid carboxyl groups formed in the oil during the bodying period are dispelled and replaced by the acidic resinous material which is much less volatile and much more heat stable, with the result that resinous and oily components are linked together.

To demonstrate the principle of

expelling volatile material

by heat-stable substances, examples taken from related fields can be cited. For instance, if stearic acid is heated with triacetin, acetic acid escapes and stearic glyceride is formed, quantitatively if an excess of stearic acid is used. Or, if run Congo copal is heated with diethyl phthalate, phthalic anhydride distills off in abundant quantities, with the Congo acids entering into the ester compound.

The process of combining coating and ink resins with drying vegetable oils takes place in several distinctly different phases. Resins of unusually high solubility can be dissolved in the oil by sufficiently long tumbling of the oil with the finely crushed resin pieces, without the help of a strong solvent. Resins of lesser solubility can be incorporated into oil combinations of homogenious appearance only through the addition of strong solvents. Most of these systems are not true dispersions of the resin in the oil, which becomes apparent on drying, when the resin-oil mixture will yield a flat, peculiarly spotted surface.

A perfect combination of resins with oils, especially of high-melting resins with polymerized oils, can be obtained only by application of heat. The

heat combining proceeds

in two subsequent steps. In the first step, resin and oil are heated to a temperature high enough to give a clear solution while held at the high temperature. In this state the two components are still only imperfectly combined, because they separate again easily, either on cooling and on addition of weak solvents. Accordingly, the drying and gloss characteristics of such combinations are poor.

In the second step resin and oil are heat-combined to such a degree that the combination will not show any cloudiness through separation, either on cooling or on thinning with mineral spirits of low solvency. In this stage, perfect physical homogeneity is obtained, yielding films of high gloss and smooth flow.

When the completely heat combined resin-oil mixture is

submitted to continued heating, further changes take place. In the case of highly inactivated resins, no chemical reactions take place between the two substances and the oil component polymerizes separately. In the case of strongly reactive resins, particularly in the presence of slow bodying oils, a chemical linkage between resin and oil occurs, which is not accompanied by a polymerization of the oil phase. In the majority of cases both chemical reactions and oil polymerization take place simultaneously.

The protective and decorative characteristics of resin oil combinations, obtained by processes in which

chemical reactions

play a substantial part, are superior to those of combinations made by processes in which no chemical interaction is involved.

Chemical reactivities, as a rule, speed up bodying action and at the same time have a beneficial effect on drying properties. Experience shows that, with a few exceptions, resin-oil combinations which body fast have good drying speeds, and that slow bodying combinations will dry slowly.

Such reactivities also are beneficial to the stability of varnishes and enamels on storage in the can, because true chemical reaction between resin and oil decidedly counteracts a continued polymerization of the oil portion, manifested in the after-bodying of the varnish or enamel.

Furthermore, chemical reactivities are of utmost importance for the building up of the

chemical and mechanical characteristics

of the dried surface coating film. Resistance to water, chemicals and weathering influences is improved, because resin and oil molecules are linked together at reactive points which, by their very nature, are weak spots, open to chemical attacks.

By their linking up they disappear, reducing the number of vulnerable points in the resin-oil combination.

Chemical reactivities also change fundamentally the mechanical properties of the films formed by the drying of the oil-resin combination. For instance, if a solution of a hard resin in a solvent is added to an oil at room temperature, no reaction takes place and the effect is that the flexibility of the oil film is lowered to a degree proportional to the amount of resin added. This well-known fact forms the basis for the Kauri value method of determining flexibility. It is also utilized in using cold cuts of hard resins as additions to rubbing varnishes and sealers, to obtain the required rubbing and sanding properties.

Entirely different mechanical effects are obtained if the resin acts chemically on the oil. There is no longer any proportionality between the amount of resin added to the oil and the change in mechanical film properties. The determination of Kauri values supplies conclusive evidence of this and, at the same time, demonstrates that chemical reaction improves flexibility far beyond that obtained from a physical mixture. To give an example, a varnish based on an acid-condensed butyl phenol resin is compared to a varnish based on a coumarone resin, both made with linseed oil and by the same cooking procedure. To pass the 100% Kauri reduction test, the reactive phenol resin requires 25 gallons of oil, whereas the entirely indifferent coumarone resin requires twice as much, *i.e.* 50 gallons of oil.

The interesting technical effects described previously are accompanied by a

molecular enlargement

which consists of the linking together of the high molecular resin molecule with the more or less polymerized oil molecule, forming one large aggregate which, on further heating, continues to grow in size. The product formed by this type of agglomeration of resinous and oily components is necessarily different in properties from a product formed by the association of low molecular mixed esters which, before their enlargement, contain in every molecule, both fatty and rosin acid radicals.

The type and size of the molecular arrangement in the resin-oil combinations under consideration, appear from the following example. One part of a modified phenol resin, having a molecular weight of 1400, was melted at low temperature, with two parts of a bodied linseed oil having a molecular weight of 1375. The molecular weight of the homogeniously fused mixture was found to be 1400. The mixture was then heated to 300° C., held there for two hours and its molecular weight was determined. It was found to be 2200. When each of the two components was heated alone in the same way, the resin gained about 100 units and the oil gained about 250 units, so that a molecular weight of 1600 could have been expected for the combination, if no chemical linkage had taken place. The actually determined figure of 2200 proved that a considerable percentage of resin and oil molecules had formed large molecular aggregates.

The many different ways in which resin and oils can enter into combinations with each other are reflected by the various activities of the coating and ink resins under consideration.

Modified maleic resins

represent the resin types which show little or no reactivities on cooking with oils, unless they are made with an amount of esterifying alcohol which exceeds the quantity necessary to neutralize the free acids present.

If normal maleic resins are heated with oils, the oil phase bodies separately and continued heat polymerization of such mixtures leads to a point at which the resinous and oily components cease to be compatible with each other, and the batch starts to segregate gelatinous particles. This inertness also has a very important consequence for maleic resin varnishes on storage. The varnish actually contains resin and oil dissolved in the varnish solvent as separate units. Under the influence of the cobalt drier present, the oil portion itself continues to polymerize, causing increase in viscosity or afterbodying of the varnish. The polymerization of the oil proper may proceed to a degree that maleic resin and oil become insoluble in each other, resulting in the complete gelation of the varnish.

Pure phenol resins are distinguished by particularly high reactivity with oils, details of which are given in the chapter on

phenol resins.

They act through their free hydroxyl groups, of which two different types are present, *i.e.* phenolic hydroxyl groups, originating from the phenol used for the production of the resin, and alcoholic hydroxyl groups, coming from the action of the formaldehyde on the phenol.

Acid-condensed pure phenolics are less reactive with oils than alkali-condensed resins. Acid-condensed resins do not react through their phenolic hydroxyls, which remain inert with oils. Their reactivity depends on their alcoholic hydroxyls, which are able to esterify free fatty carboxyls formed in the oil during the varnish cooking process, thereby causing a chemical bond between resin and oil.

Alkali-condensed pure phenolics possess the same sort of reactivity, but in addition have the ability to react directly with neutral oils through their phenolic hydroxyls. This double reactivity makes alkali-condensed pure phenolics particularly valuable for oil combinations, producing an extremely high degree of chemical resistance and waterproofness.

The oil reactivity of

modified phenol resins

is governed by the same principles as the alkali-condensed pure phenolics, because they contain the same type of phenolic and alcoholic hydroxyl groups. Their number is considerably smaller but large enough to cause good oil reactivity. As described later in detail, the modified phenolics contain the alkali-catalyzed formaldehyde condensates of para tertiary butyl phenol, para tertiary amyl phenol, or of bis phenol in the form of a solution or dispersion in the rosin component. The phenolic and alcoholic hydroxyl groups are not linked with the rosin, but are free for reactivities with oil. During the varnish-making process, the phenolic hydroxyls attach themselves directly to reactive points in the chain of the oil molecule, whereas the alcoholic hydroxyl groups enter into esterification with acidic groups of the oil, present initially or formed by decomposition during the process. The twofold reaction produces a very firm linkage of resin and oil with the phenolic ingredient so intimately combined, that it cannot be eliminated any more even by fusing with alkali.

Like the combination of modified phenolics with oils, the linkage of oils with

copal-type synthetics

is also of a twofold nature and, therefore, of a particularly stable character. Details on the new class of copal-type synthetic resins are later described; they are of particular interest, because these resins combine, in one group, the valuable qualities of synthetic resins as well as those of natural gums.

Copal-type synthetics are characterized by the presence of free hydroxyl groups, originating from the component raw materials, and by the presence of heat stable, non-volatile resinous acid anhydrides, which are firmly attached to the resin molecule and which are formed during resin production.

The first named groups effect a tie between resin and oil by their ability to esterify with fatty acid carboxyls. The last named groups link resin and oil together by their capability to expel, at the high temperature of varnish cooking, volatile acidic groups of the oil, and to take their place in the molecular arrangement.

Chapter II

Phenol Resins

In the manufacture of surface coatings and printing inks both pure phenol resins and rosin-modified phenol resins are used. Only the more important types, representing the two resin classes, are discussed in this technological study.

Limitation to a few types

is necessary because of the amazingly large number of phenol resins. On the other hand, discussion of a limited number of resins is sufficient to clarify resin structure and properties because most of the possible variations are due to the individual properties of the phenols used to produce the phenol formaldehyde condensates. If the peculiarities of the different phenols are known, the character of the resulting resins can be predicted.

PURE PHENOL RESINS

From a theoretical point of view, the phenolic component in phenol resins may vary through the whole range of phenols, from the plain carbolic acid, through alkyl and aryl-substituted phenols, up to the phenols with high molecular substituents, in this way possibly embracing more than fifty known compounds.

The formaldehyde condensate of the unsubstituted phenol, *i.e.* of plain carbolic acid, does not dissolve in oil; however, it can be made oil-soluble by heat, which combines the low molecular formaldehyde condensate with rosin. The rosin combination of the unsubstituted phenol does not retard the drying of oxidizing oils, as is the case with many substituted phenols. Its original color is pale; however, when exposed to oxidation in a drying varnish film, it discolors temporarily with a distinct yellow hue, which bleaches out again after the varnish film has dried completely. It is difficult to find a reasonable explanation for the temporary formation of a yellow dyestuff in the drying varnish film, when compounds of unsubstituted phenol are present.

The characteristics of the cresol condensates depend largely on the position of the methyl group which forms the substituent. The ortho compound produces oil-soluble resins of poor color, bodying and drying characteristics; the meta compound, in addition to such drawbacks, produces resins of insufficient solubility. The para cresol condensates, on the other hand, are soluble in oils, have fair color stability, good bodying properties, and dry fairly well with soft oils. For high quality coating and ink resins, their degree of light stability and solubility, is not satisfactory.

The properties of xylenol condensates depend much on the position of the two methyl groups present as substituents. The existence of four different types of xylenols is possible and all of them are actually available, as such, or in mixtures. Their light stability is fair when the para position is taken, and is poor in the other derivatives. Their fusibility and solubility are generally satisfactory, as are bodying and drying characteristics, provided quick and hard drying oils, and not straight linseed oil, are used.

The characteristics of alkyl phenols with higher molecular substituents, the main representatives of which are

the butyl and amyl phenols

are outstanding, if the substituents are in the para position. They are distinguished particularly by yielding resins of unusual color stability and solubility. The substituents in all alkyl-substituted phenols are of an entirely saturated type and, therefore, show no indication of a direct reaction between the substituent groups and oils.

Aryl-substituted phenols are as important from the varnish maker's standpoint as are the alkyl phenols. The outstanding type in this field is the *p,p'*-dihydroxy diphenyl dimethyl methane, in short called bis phenol. While its formaldehyde condensate is insoluble in oils, it can be incorporated into varnishes after it has been solubilized by rosin.

Bis phenol resins

display better color retention, hardness, bodying and drying characteristics than most other phenol resins.

Other important aryl-substituted phenols are the phenyl phenols, with the para-substituted type used widely for resin making. Except for a tendency to discolor in the drying film and a poor solubility of the oil combination in mineral spirits, its resinous condensates possess excellent varnish characteristics of bodying, drying and durability. The last named property is probably due to the fact that the substituent, *i.e.*, the highly unsaturated phenyl group itself, contains a number of active points free for a chemical combination with oils. The para cyclohexyl phenol has a place in resin manufacture generally, but not for coating resins, because of the slow bodying action of the condensate.

In addition to the phenol types mentioned, there exists a number of very interesting phenol compounds mostly with high molecular substituents. The more important among these are the mixed isomers of di-isobutyl phenol, thymol, carvacrol, cardanol, resorcinol, salicylic acid and its derivatives, isomeric mixtures of terpene phenols, and others. Only a few of these types have found commercial application for coating and ink resins.

Surveying the various phenol classes from the varnish maker's viewpoint, a few simple rules appear to govern the relationship between phenol types and the technical resin properties with regard to color stability, solubility, bodying speed, drying characteristics and water resistance. These

rules are discussed

in the following paragraphs.

The best color stability is shown by the para-substituted phenols. Ortho- and most of the meta-substituted products yield strongly yellowing resins. The discoloration, which takes place while the resin oil film is drying, is due to the formation of a chromophore group which, according to generally accepted views, is a para-substituted complex. If the para position is occupied, the color creating group cannot be formed, accounting for the superior light fastness of para-substituted phenols. The same color stable structure is contained in the binuclear bis phenol, in which the two phenol rings are linked together at their para position by means of a group derived from acetone.

The best solubility is produced by ortho- and para-substituted phenols, whereas products substituted in the meta position have a strong tendency to form insoluble resins. As a rule, solubility of the resins is dependent less on the position than on the type of the phenol substituent, with the effect that alkyl substitution produces better solubility than aryl substitution.

Position and type of substituent also govern the drying and bodying characteristics of phenol resins. The influence of the position of the substituent is shown by the fact that all ortho compounds are much slower drying or bodying than the corresponding para compounds and, in some cases, actually act as antioxidants. The role of the type of substituent is evidenced by the fact that para tertiary amyl and butyl derivatives are considerably slower drying and bodying than the phenyl compounds or the bis phenol products. This difference in drying and bodying characteristics is noticeable in combination with China wood oil or oiticica oil, and becomes very pronounced in combination with soft oils, as for instance, linseed oil or dehydrated castor oil.

The degree of water resistance produced by phenol resins in coating films depends on the degree of their reactivity with oils; in other words, the more oil-reactive the phenol condensate is, the more pronounced is the waterproofing effect on the oil. As a rule, the increase in film resistance by the chemical action of phenol resins on oils is far beyond that which could be expected, and is of the order of magnitude that even additions of as low as 10% of phenolic body to the oil produce a surprising increase in resistance. The main factor governing oil reactivity is the structure of the formaldehyde condensate and the number of reactive phenolic and alcoholic hydroxyl groups present, as will be later demonstrated. The type and the position of the phenolic substituent is of lesser importance.

The previous comments on phenol types have made it clear that the special requirements for the properties of useful coating and ink resins with regard to color stability, drying, bodying and solubility, limit the types of phenols suitable for this purpose, to the group of para tertiary butyl and amyl phenols and the *p,p'*-dihydroxy diphenyl dimethyl methane, *i.e.* the binuclear bis phenol.

In the process of manufacturing pure phenol resins, often called 100% phenol resins, the phenols are first

combined with formaldehyde

in varying quantities and using different catalysts. As a rule, an acid catalyst adds one mol of formaldehyde to one mol of phenol, and an alkaline catalyst links up two or more mols of formaldehyde with one mol of phenol. Both acid- and alkali-catalyzed condensates of para tertiary butyl and amyl phenols are used for the production of pure phenol resins for coating and ink purposes.

The properties and reactivities of both classes of pure phenol resins are discussed in detail in the following comments. Included in these comments are interesting observations on the alkali-catalyzed formaldehyde condensate of the bis phenol. This condensation product is not of any great importance for the production of pure phenol resins, but plays an important part in the manufacture of modified phenolics.

The condensation products of para tertiary butyl and amyl phenols with formaldehyde,

obtained by acidic condensation

can chemically be considered as phenol alcohols, because they contain free alcoholic hydroxyl groups. They are viscous substances of opaque, whitish appearance which, on heating, lose water and gradually harden into clear resins. The first resin-like product formed in the process of condensing para tertiary butyl phenol with formaldehyde has a molecular weight of 500 to 600, which corresponds to an aggregation of three individual molecules of the mono-molecular condensate. During the heat hardening of the resin, more molecules combine and the molecular weight increases. When the resin is heated to 170° C., five single molecules have combined and a molecular weight of 850 to 900 is reached. The melting point of the resin at this stage is about 135° C., *i.e.* it possesses considerable hardness. On further heating, the molecular weight increases to nearly 1100, *i.e.* to the equivalent of six molecules.

Formaldehyde condensates of para tertiary amyl phenols condense under heat in a similar way, except that the melting points are lower. At a melting point of about 90° C., a molecular weight of 650 to 700 is found, which, on further heat hardening, increases to values corresponding to an agglomeration of about five single molecules.

The number of six molecules seems to be the upper limit of molecular association for acid-condensed alkyl phenol resins. On further heating very little, if any, changes occur.

On heating the resins alone up to 200° C., no foam is visible, and the material remains permanently fusible and retains its complete solubility in oils. It is only at temperatures above 200° C. that the resin shows slight signs of decomposition, being split into formaldehyde and free phenol. If the acid-condensed resins are heated with drying oils very little, if any, foaming occurs, but a definite and technically valuable reaction takes place nevertheless, at varnish-making temperatures, as will be explained in detail. Generally speaking, it can be stated that the amount of foam, developed in cooking phenol resins with oils, is not a measure of the beneficial effect of the pure phenol resin on the oil. It is possible, for instance, that a non-foaming type produces better water resistance than a foaming resin type.

Phenol-formaldehyde condensation products,

obtained by alkaline condensation

are of a different nature from those produced by acid catalysts. Para tertiary butyl and amyl phenols, and also bis phenol, yield formaldehyde condensates under alkaline conditions, which are thin, to slightly viscous, liquids. Chemically they are considered phenol alcohols in a low molecular state which, on heating, undergo progressive self-condensation, gain in viscosity and finally resinify. The process of resinification is accompanied by the development of foam due to the evaporation of water, which is formed in the normal course of every phenol formaldehyde condensation. Under continued heating, the products finally gelatinize into infusible and insoluble masses. The speed of resinification, and the temperature of gelation, depend on the type of the phenol and the amount of formaldehyde present in the condensate.

The self-condensation of the bis phenol product proceeds so quickly, even at low temperatures, that it is difficult to stop and check it at an intermediate, unfinished stage, while the resin is still fusible. The progress of the condensation of alkyl phenol-formaldehyde products, on the other hand, is controlled more easily and can be stopped during the course of the reaction. For most practical purposes, the

resinification of alkyl phenol condensates

is not carried to completion but checked, either at an early stage, while the material is still liquid, or at a later stage, when the condensate has become a hard resin. As a rule, the

FIGURE 5. Surface of a pure phenol resin during cooling.

resin producer uses the liquid material for making pure and modified phenolics, whereas the varnish maker works with the resinous product having a melting point of about 80-90° C.

The stopping of the resinification process in actual practice of resin manufacture is done by pouring the liquid resin into shallow flat cooling pans. If unloaded into ordinary large drums which contain close to five hundred pounds of resin, the resin would continue to resinify, and enter into a severe exothermic reaction, causing detrimental foaming and gel formation.

When poured out on a cooling surface in thin layer, the resin hardens as fast as it is poured, and strange surface effects are obtained, as shown in *Figure 5*, resembling the ripples on the quiet waters of a lake on a moonlight night.

To gain a better insight into the mechanism of the resinification process, the

changes in molecular weights

during the hardening are determined. The molecular weight of an alkali-catalyzed condensate of para tertiary butyl phenol in its initial, slightly viscous form, is about 400, indicating a double molecule. When it is resinified into a hard resin with a melting point of about 90° C., by heating it to 130° C. its molecular weight is 750 to 800, indicating the association of 3 or 4 single molecules. On further heating the molecular enlargement continues and at a temperature of 230° C. reaches an association of 5 or 6 molecules, equivalent to a molecular weight of 1150. The molecular aggregation proceeds, on continued heating and under the influence of temperature, until 6 or 7 molecules are combined with each other. This stage is reached shortly before the resin converts into the insoluble and infusible state.

The resinous condensate, in which 6 or 7 single molecules unite into one group, is probably the phenolic ingredient present in rosin-modified phenolics, basing this assumption on the fact that the molecular weight of such rosin-modified phenolics is of an equal order of magnitude. On prolonged heating during the maturing process as previously described, further enlargement of the phenolic molecule to possibly 7 or 8 combined units takes place, made possible by processes of molecular association during the maturing procedure.

The molecular weight of a liquid, alkali-catalyzed, bis phenol condensate obtained at room temperature, is only slightly higher than that of the monomolecular compound. The monomeric compound has a molecular weight of 318, assuming the condensation of one mol of bis phenol with three mols of formaldehyde. Dehydrating this compound by heating it, under vacuum, up to 65° C., its molecular weight increases to 425 and continues to grow during the resinification until the resin becomes insoluble. If, due to the presence of rosin, the condensate is prevented from converting into the insoluble state, the molecular aggregation may progress, like that of para tertiary butyl or amyl phenol condensates, to a point where 6 or 8 molecules are linked with each other. Substantial evidence for this assumption is found in the following figures. A non-esterified, rosin-modified bis phenol resin, prepared from three parts of rosin and one part of bis phenol condensate, has a molecular weight of 1100. Considering that during the processing the rosin component has increased its molecular size to about 600, *i.e.* has formed double molecules, a molecular weight of 2600 would result for the phenolic compound, which is very close to the equivalent of eight molecular units.

The technical evaluation of alkali-condensed pure phenol resins often is carried out by determining the increase of the melting point of ester gum, caused by the addition of a given amount of phenol resins, after the mixture has been treated under standardized conditions. The increases are substantial. If, for instance, 100 parts of ester gum, with a melting point of 90° C., are reacted with 25 parts of an alkali-condensed para tertiary butyl phenol resin, a product is obtained which has a melting point of 140° C., *i.e.* the hardness of the ester gum is increased by 50° C., and by applying simple arithmetic, the figure also indicates that the phenolic body present in the hardened ester gum possesses a melting point of about 340° C., which is extremely high.

Another method of

evaluating the technical usefulness

of alkali-condensed pure phenol resins consists in determining the increase in viscosity undergone by varnish linseed oil when heat-treated with a given amount of the resin under standardized conditions. This test is limited to the alkyl phenolics, because bis-phenol condensates are not soluble in oils, and will remain in solution only in free rosin or in highly acidic rosin products.

PHENOLIC AND ALCOHOLIC HYDROXYL GROUPS

The main value of both alkali and acid-condensed pure phenol resins lies in their ability to react chemically with other resins and oils. A systematic investigation has shown that this ability is based on the reactivity of the free hydroxyl groups, which are present in pure phenolics. Two different types are present, *i.e.* the phenolic hydroxyls, originating from the phenol used in the production of the resin, and the alcoholic hydroxyls formed by the action of the formaldehyde on the phenol. By defining the individual characteristics of each of the two classes of hydroxyl groups, and by determining in exact percentage figures the amount of each of them present in the phenol-formaldehyde condensate, the pure phenolics can be accurately evaluated with regard to their reactivity with resinous and oily substances. This evaluation in turn establishes their usefulness in coatings and printing inks.

Both phenolic and alcoholic hydroxyl groups can be determined analytically with satisfactory accuracy through applying the usual methods of determining

acid and acetyl values.

The acid value, arrived at by alkali titration, indicates the number of free phenolic hydroxyl groups, because they behave like carboxyl groups in the titration. The acetyl value, obtained as the differential of the saponification values of the acetylated and the non-acetylated resin, is the base for calculating the total number of both phenolic and alcoholic hydroxyls. The difference between total hydroxyl value and phenolic hydroxyl value indicates the number of free alcoholic hydroxyl groups.

Acid, saponification and acetyl values are usually expressed through the number of milligrams of potassium hydroxide entering into reaction with one gram of resin. In the following calculations and considerations, all values are uniformly converted into hydroxyl values by applying the factor of 17/56 to the potassium hydroxide figures. The hydroxyl values given represent the number of milligrams of hydroxyl groups present in one gram of resin.

The exact determination of

the phenolic hydroxyl groups

is based on the fact that the pure phenol resins under consideration have an alkali titration value if titrated by the method used for determination of acid values of resins. Since neither carboxyl groups nor saponifiable substances are present, and since the alcoholic hydroxyls which are present do not react with alkali, the alkali titration value indicates the phenolic hydroxyl groups which are free and reactive.

In this way the number of free phenolic hydroxyl groups was determined for five different resins, *i.e.* for acid-catalyzed para tertiary amyl and butyl phenol resins, both condensed with one mol of formaldehyde; for alkali-catalyzed para tertiary amyl and butyl phenol resins, both condensed with two mols of formaldehyde; and for an alkali-condensed bis phenol resin with three mols of formaldehyde.

The resins investigated were free of residual acid catalysts, sometimes used in the preparation of phenolics, which would largely influence the results of the alkali titration. All resins were of the hard and brittle type, as obtained by dehydration under heat and vacuum, with top temperatures between 80° and 150° C.

The interesting figures obtained are recorded in *Table 2*. The first column of this table gives the phenolic hydroxyl values determined for the five resins under investigation. The second column gives the theoretical phenolic hydroxyl values computed for the monomolecular condensates, from which the resins are produced; these values represent the total amount of phenolic hydroxyls originally present. The third column compares phenolic hydroxyl values before and after resinification and gives the relative amount of hydroxyls left free for reaction, in per cent of their quantity present before the self-condensation sets in.

Table 2. Change of Phenolic Hydroxyl Values of Phenol-formaldehyde Condensates During Resinification

Type of Phenol-Formaldehyde Condensate	*Phenolic Hydroxyl Value of Resins (determined by Titration)*	*Phenolic Hydroxyl Value of Monomeric Phenol-Formaldehyde Condensate (computed from theoretical formula)*	*Phenolic Hydroxyl Value of Resins in Per Cent of Value of the Monomeric Product*
Acid-condensed amyl phenol	24	87	27%
butyl phenol	26	95	27%
Alkali-condensed amyl phenol	16	75	21%
butyl phenol	18	81	22%
bis phenol	15	106	14%

The survey in *Table 2* shows clearly that, in the process of resinification, the major part of the phenolic hydroxyl groups disappears. The average phenolic hydroxyl value of the monomeric product drops from about 90 to an average of about 20 for the resinified material. On the other hand, the survey demonstrates convincingly that substantial percentages of free and reactive phenolic hydroxyl groups are left in the heat hardened resins, amounting to more than 10 and less than 30% of the originally present number of hydroxyls.

The residual free phenolic hydroxyl groups under discussion are distinguished by great stability. They are, in particular,

very heat stable.

Accordingly, the values for phenolic hydroxyls do not decrease when the resins are heated to varnish-making temperatures. This practically and theoretically very important fact is proved by the following simple experiments:

If acid-condensed alkyl phenol resins are heated with paraffin oil, the figure of alkali titration does not decrease, indicating that phenolic hydroxyl groups do not disappear. This behavior can be expected, because the solvent is inert and no foaming occurs.

If alkali-condensed alkyl phenol resins are heated up with paraffin oil, heavy foaming takes place, but no change in alkali titration values can be observed. For instance, one hundred parts of paraffin oil were heated with 25 parts of an alkali-condensed para tertiary amyl phenol resin of an acid value of 55. When the temperature of 240° C. was reached, the foam subsided and a sample was taken. The heating was continued and another sample was taken at 270° C. The alkali titration did not change during the total procedure, in spite of the heavy foaming. Because the foam was not due to any activity of the phenolic hydroxyl group, it must be caused by a reaction of the alcoholic hydroxyl groups, as will be later explained.

As shown in *Table 2*, alkali-condensed bis phenol resins also contain a substantial amount of

residual free phenolic hydroxyl

groups, although in percentage the amount is lower than in alkyl phenol products. Their heat stability cannot be investigated by heating with paraffin oil, because on heating with paraffin oil, the resins become insoluble and cannot be titrated. For this purpose, however, ordinary rosin proves to be a very suitable solvent. Bis phenol condensates dissolve completely in liquid rosin, stay in solution on heating, and do not enter into any esterification which would lower the acid value.

The following determination proves the heat stability of free phenolic hydroxyl groups in bis phenol resins. At low temperature, one hundred parts of rosin were fused together with 25 parts of alkali-condensed bis phenol resin. The acid value of this mixture was determined as 142. After heating it to 270° C., and holding it at 270° for two hours, the acid value dropped to 126, *i.e.* 16 units. When rosin was treated alone under exactly comparable conditions, the decrease was 20 units. Therefore, the actual loss in acidity was the equivalent of the rosin part alone, and it follows that the number of free phenolic hydroxyl groups has not changed by the heating process. Foaming that actually takes place is the result of a self-condensation of the alcoholic hydroxyl groups also present in the resin.

It appears from the various tests previously described, that the free phenolic hydroxyls, in both acid and alkali-condensed resins of the type under discussion, possess extreme stability under heat. They are also

comparatively stable chemically

and do not react with organic acids, unless induced by strong catalysts which, however, are not present in the chemical reactions of resin or varnish manufacture. Phenolic hydroxyl groups can be acetylated by the use of acetic anhydride, but remain inactive with low molecular organic acids, and do not show any reactivity with high molecular acids of either resinous or fatty character.

The lack of reactivity with resinous acids is proved by the fact that no change of acid value occurs when pure phenol resins are heated with rosin. A proof for the same inertness with fatty acids can be found in the behavior of acid-condensed alkyl phenol resins, when these resin types are heated with linseed oil fatty acids. Partial esterification of the fatty acids takes place in this case due to the presence of alcoholic hydroxyl groups, but complete neutrality is not obtained, because the phenolic hydroxyls which act as acidic groups remain unsaturated.

Phenolic hydroxyls also remain inert with the reactive double bond in rosin, as can be shown indirectly by heating hydrogenated rosin, in which this double bond is blocked, with an alkali-condensed para tertiary butyl phenol resin. This resin dissolves readily in the hydrogenated rosin and increases the melting point of the hydrogenated rosin to the same extent as that of ordinary rosin, proving that the double bond plays no chemical role in this procedure.

The relative inertness of phenolic hydroxyl groups, however, has

one very important exception

i.e. the pronounced reactivity of phenolic hydroxyls of alkali-condensed resins with drying oils. To demonstrate this unique phenomenon, the changes in acid values of combinations of such resins with oil were determined. 100 parts of a linseed oil of an acid value of 2.5 were fused with 25 parts of an acid-condensed and 25 parts of an alkali-condensed para tertiary amyl phenol resin. The batches were heated to 270° C., and held at this temperature for one hour. Acid values were taken at the beginning and at the end of the run. A blank test with linseed oil alone showed no substantial change in acid value. The results are reported in *Table 3* giving the changes in acidity of resin-oil combinations.

Table 3. Change of Acidity in Resin-oil Combination on Heating

	100 Parts of Linseed Oil Heated with 25 Parts of an	
	Acid-Condensed Amyl Phenol Resin	*Alkali-Condensed Amyl Phenol Resin*
Acid value at the start of experiment at 110° C.	18.8	13.5
Acid value at the end of experiment at 270° C.	18.2	4.5
Decrease in acid value	0.6	9.0

Table 3 shows that the phenolic hydroxyl groups in the acid-condensed resin remain inert with oils, inasmuch as the acid value of the reaction mixture practically does not change. But it proves by the spectacular drop in acid value undergone by the reaction mixture containing the alkali-condensed resin, that the phenolic hydroxyl groups in this resin class possess high reactivity with oil. Due to this reactivity, their number is greatly reduced during the heating process.

Corresponding tests with other drying oils, including dehydrated castor oil, gave practically the same results.

Whereas this interesting reactivity has been demonstrated by experiment only for alkali-condensed para tertiary amyl and butyl phenol resins, it can be assumed, by way of analogy, that the phenolic hydroxyls in bis phenol resins possess the same type of reactivity with oil, the only proviso being that the bis phenol resin is kept in a soluble and liquid condition, as in the case of rosin-modified phenolics.

The type of chemical reaction, which links the phenolic hydroxyl groups of alkali-condensed resins with the oil is not known; however it is established that the linkage is not accompanied by the forming of water. It can be shown by experiment that the amount of water eliminated is the same, whether the resin is heated with the reactive linseed oil or with the inert paraffin oil. The various

structural theories

that have been offered as explanation of such reactivities are supported by little experimental evidence.

One opinion, contrary to experimental evidence, is based on the assumption that the hydroxyl group links up with an aliphatic hydrogen of the fatty acid chain which, according to this idea, develops enough mobility, at varnish-making temperatures, to permit such linkage. Another opinion ascribes the reaction to the entrance of the phenolic hydroxyl groups into the unsaturated groups of the oils, quite in accordance with the fact that the degree of phenolic reactivity increases noticeably with the degree of unsaturation of the oils.

These theories mean little to the resin user and varnish maker. The important fact is, that pronounced chemical reactions actually occur, producing valuable technical effects, when alkali-condensed phenol resins are heated with drying oils in the varnish-making process.

Together with phenolic hydroxyls, all pure phenol resins contain

alcoholic hydroxyl groups

which are of equal, if not higher, importance to the technical usefulness of the resins. The quantitative determination of the alcoholic hydroxyl groups is carried out by subjecting them to the orthodox method of acetylation and determination of acetyl values with a few slight variations in the analytical procedure. In this procedure 5 grams of the resin are refluxed for two hours with 15 grams of acetic anhydride. Then the excess of acetic anhydride is hydrolized by boiling with water and the resinous material is washed with water until neutral. It is advisable to dissolve the resin in a small amount of xylol to assure the elimination of free acetic acid. The acetylated resin is finally saponified with 100 c.c. of $1N$ alcoholic potassium hydroxide by refluxing for one hour and the excess of alkali is determined by back titration with $1N$ hydrochloric acid. The figure thus obtained represents the saponification value of the acetylated resin, and indicates the total hydroxyl value for both phenolic and alcoholic hydroxyl groups together. By deducting from this figure the phenolic hydroxyl value previously determined, the value for the alcoholic hydroxyl groups is obtained.

The accuracy of determining acetyl values is limited in the case of most synthetic resins, because of certain side reactions which may take place during the acetylation. The accuracy is satisfactory in the case of pure phenolics, here under discussion, all of which are soluble in acetic anhydride and remain soluble after resinification. In case determinations are made for resins which have been resinified at temperatures lower than 140° C., the values obtained apply to resinification temperatures of 140° C., which is the boiling point of acetic anhydride. This temperature does not deviate substantially from actual conditions in the production of oil-soluble pure phenolics and the figures, therefore, are valid for a great deal of commercial resin.

The previously described analytical

method of acetylation

was used to determine the alcoholic hydroxyl values for three commercial resins, *i.e.* for an acid-condensed and an alkali-condensed butyl phenol resin and for an alkali-condensed bis-phenol resin. The results are reported in *Table 4*.

The first column gives the alcoholic hydroxyl values calculated for the monomolecular substances; the second column records the values actually found for the condensates, resinified by heat hardening at a top temperature of 140° C., and the third column gives the alcoholic hydroxyl values for the resins, after they have been heated up to 250° C. The last named determination could not be made with the bis phenol resin because it became insoluble at that temperature.

Table 4.　Change of Alcoholic Hydroxyl Values in Pure Phenolics on Heating

Type of Pure Phenolic	Alcoholic Hydroxyl Values of Monomolecular Products	Alcoholic Hydroxyl Values of Resins Hardened at 140° C.	Alcoholic Hydroxyl Values of Resins Heated to 250° C.
Acid-condensed Butyl phenol resin	95	95	95
Alkali-condensed Butyl phenol resin	162	120	67
Alkali-condensed Bis phenol resin	160	124	—

The table establishes very

important rules

with regard to the amounts of alcoholic hydroxyl groups and with reference to their changes during the heat hardening process.　The acid condensed resin has a hydroxyl value identical with that of the monomeric product and does not decrease under heat treatment.　The hardening, therefore, must be entirely due to an interaction of the phenolic hydroxyl groups, leaving practically all of the alcoholic hydroxyl groups free for reaction.

The alkali-condensed resins have very high alcoholic hydroxyl values before resinification, due to the comparatively large amounts of formaldehyde employed in their manufacture.　When resinified at 140° C., both alkali-condensed alkyl and bis phenol resins retain a high percentage of free alcoholic hydroxyl groups, *i.e.* about three-quarters of the quantity present in the monomolecular product.

If heated to 250° C., the alkali-condensed para tertiary butyl phenol resin loses, due to self-condensation, about one-third of all its alcoholic hydroxyl groups, though leaving a substantial amount free for further reactivities.　The quantity of free alcoholic hydroxyls is nearly as large as that of the phenolic hydroxyl groups.

The alcoholic hydroxyl groups in both acid- and alkali-condensed resins have interesting properties.

Neither reacts with rosin

as is shown by heating the phenolic condensates with rosin at 270° C. for several hours. The small decrease in acid value which occurs is equivalent to that which is caused by the decarboxylation of the rosin itself, as proved by a blank test. If an interaction between the alcoholic hydroxyl of the phenolic body and the carboxyl of the rosin took place, a very considerable drop in acid value would ensue. An activity at reactive points other than the carboxyl groups is a theoretical possibility. That such a reaction, however, does not take place is shown by heating the phenol resin with rosin to 200° C., and determining the amount of water that escapes. This amount is exactly the same when the resin is heated either alone, with rosin, or with the inert paraffin oil.

When alkali-condensed resins are heated, a small amount of formaldehyde and volatile decomposition products, such as certain dialdehydes, always starts to develop at temperatures about 50° higher than the temperature at which the water is split off. The amounts of such decomposition products are negligible and too small to influence the above considerations.

The alcoholic hydroxyl groups of the acid- and alkali-condensed resins under discussion do not react with acid-free drying oils.

Oil reactivity

is not expected from acid-condensed resins, because no foaming occurs on heating; it might have been expected in the case of alkali-condensed resins, because their fusing with oils is accompanied by spectacular foaming. Proof for the non-reactivity of the alcoholic hydroxyl groups of pure phenolics with neutral oils is brought out by determining the quantity of water liberated in such procedures. The amount of water liberated is the same, if the resin is heated with the wholly unreactive paraffin oil, or if it is heated with neutral linseed oil, China wood oil or dehydrated castor oil. Furthermore, the amount of water liberated by heating resin and oil separately checks very closely with that given off by heating resin and oil together. This observation proves at the same time that the reaction previously mentioned, which occurs between the phenolic hydroxyl groups of alkali-condensed resins, is not of a type that eliminates water.

Contrary to their inertness toward neutral oils and rosin, the alcoholic hydroxyl groups have a pronounced

tendency to react with fatty acids

and acid oils, *i.e.* a strong tendency to esterification. This reactivity is demonstrated by two simple experiments with acid- and alkali-condensed para tertiary butyl phenol resins, reacted with linseed oil fatty acid. In carrying out such experiments, 100 parts of linseed oil fatty acid were fused with 25 parts of each of the resins. The batches were heated to 270° C. within two hours and held at this temperature for two hours. Samples for acid value determination were taken at the beginning and end of the test. A blank test showing the decrease in the acid value of the fatty acid when heated alone was also carried out. *Table 5* records the change of acidity of such fatty acid resin combinations.

Table 5.   Change of Acidity of Phenol Resin—Fatty Acid
Combinations on Heating

	Acid Value of Fatty Acid Alone	Acid Value of Fatty Acid Combined With Acid-condensed Butyl Phenol Resin	Acid Value of Fatty Acid Combined With Alkali-condensed Butyl Phenol Resin
Heated to 110° C.	195	175	170
Heated at 270° C.	185	110	105
Decrease of acid value	10	65	65

The values given in *Table 5* prove that a vivid reaction takes place, leading to a considerable decrease in acidity, with both acid- and alkali-condensed resins. By adding more phenol resin, the acidity can be further reduced. In the case of acid-condensed resins, the acidity of the mixture cannot decrease below the level produced by the phenolic hydroxyl groups, whereas the acidity of the reaction mixture with alkali-condensed resins may decline further, due to a direct linkage of the phenolic hydroxyls with the fatty acid chain.

Bis phenol condensates cannot be investigated in this simple way, because they are not soluble in fatty acids and precipitate from the batch soon after the temperature reaches 100° C. In the presence of about the same amount of free rosin, however, the bis phenol condensate is kept in solution and can show its reactivity. In a test in which a reaction mixture of fatty acid, rosin, and bis phenol condensate was heated for two hours at 260° C., the acidity was decreased by 25 units, proving that the alcoholic hydroxyl groups of the bis phenol condensate had entered into a reaction with the fatty acid and showed the same reactivity with fatty acids as the alcoholic hydroxyl groups of the alkyl phenol condensates.

The reactivity of the alcoholic hydroxyl groups of acid and alkali-condensed

phenolics with fatty acids

is of greatest technical importance in the practice of varnish making. While, as a rule, free fatty acids, as such, are not used for varnish cooking, they are either present initially in the oils used or are formed in the oils during the varnish-cooking process. Most bodied oils contain from 3 to 10% free fatty acids when loaded into the varnish kettle and more free acid is produced by decomposition of the oil during the varnish-making process. Free acid is formed at a rapid rate at temperatures above 585° F. Acid value determinations show, for instance, that at 600° F. linseed oil forms several per cent of free fatty acid during every hour of heating.

In the contact between resin and oil, most of the fatty acids originally present are quickly neutralized by the alcoholic hydroxyl groups of the phenol resin during the period when the batch is being heated to bodying temperature. When the top temperature is reached, the free acids produced by oil-splitting are then absorbed by esterification. In this way the acidity of the resin oil batch is kept at a low level, and at the same time its speed of bodying is considerably accelerated.

Similar considerations apply to the incorporation of pure phenolics into phthalic resins, provided such alkyds contain residual free fatty acids, as is often the case.

Summarizing the reactivities of

pure phenolics in the varnish kettle

the following rules can be established. Acid-condensed resins do not react directly with neutral oils either through their phenolic or through their alcoholic hydroxyl groups. They enter indirectly into a reaction with the oil through the tendency of their alcoholic hydroxyl groups to esterify the free fatty carboxyl groups with which they come into contact during the varnish-making procedure. Alkali-condensed resins react directly with neutral oils through their phenolic hydroxyl groups. In addition, they link up with oils indirectly through their alcoholic hydroxyl groups in the same way as the acid-condensed resins. Due to the twofold linkage, alkali-condensed resins yield more complex chemical structures than acid-condensed resins.

The technical effect of the pure phenolics on the process of varnish making and the

properties of the varnish film

are very pronounced. The resin-oil batches body considerably faster with the phenolics than without them, and the final viscosity reached after a given length of time is much higher than would be attained by bodying the oil alone. At the same time, the acidity of the resin-oil combination is kept low.

The dried varnish films are distinguished by unusually high elasticity and water resistance. To demonstrate this effect of the straight phenol resin, the Kauri value and the water resistance of two linseed oil varnishes were compared, one varnish based on a pure acid-condensed phenolic, the other one based on a hard coumarone resin, which is chemically inactive, the ratio of resin to oil in both cases being one to two, and all other conditions identical. The Kauri value, indicating the elasticity of the dried film, was about 100 for the phenolic resin varnish, compared to about 30 for the coumarone varnish, proving that a highly elastic compound had been formed by the chemical interaction of phenol resin and oil. Its elasticity was more than three times as high as that of the purely physical mixture of the inert coumarone resin and oil. Comparative tests of the water resistance of the two varnish films showed the same superiority of the chemically reacted oil combination over the plain physical resin-oil mixture.

ROSIN-MODIFIED PHENOLICS

The reactivities of the formaldehyde condensate of para tertiary amyl phenol, butyl phenol and bis phenol, which have been discussed in the previous chapter, form the chemical base for the manufacture and for the practical use of the so-called rosin-modified phenol resins. A detailed discussion of the chemistry involved is particularly valuable for the chemists who use modified phenolics for their own manufacturing procedures in making coatings and printing inks.

The rosin-modified phenolics under discussion, are combinations of rosin in esterified or non-esterified form with formaldehyde condensates of para tertiary alkyl-substituted

phenols or with condensates of binuclear phenols, especially
to the *p,p'*-dihydroxy diphenyl dimethyl methane, briefly
called bis phenol. In all rosin-modified phenolics of technical
importance the portion of the rosin component exceeds the
amount of the phenolic part, the percentage of the latter
varying as a rule between 10 and 40%.

The orthodox procedure of

manufacturing modified phenolics

consists in adding the phenol formaldehyde condensate to
the liquid rosin at relatively low temperature, heating the
batch until solution is obtained and foaming has subsided,
finally esterifying the melt with glycerine or other polybasic
alcohols. In exceptional cases the rosin is esterified first and
the phenol condensate is added to the rosin ester for further
processing. Occasionally, no esterification is carried out at
all in order to obtain certain characteristics, as explained
later. Ordinarily the combination of phenolic, alcoholic and
rosin components is considered to be complete when the batch
stays clear on cooling and a low acid value is reached. For
the purpose of producing special phenolic types, the resin
batch is subjected to further treatment by a process of
maturing.

The manufacture of modified phenolics started more than
twenty years ago and has grown ever since, in spite of the
constant development of new resin types of similar nature
and in spite of the emerging of entirely novel resin groups.
There is a good reason for the fact that no curtailment to the
extended use of the old established modified phenolics over
the years has resulted. The reason is simple: they combine,
in a unique manner, solubility, viscosity, drying characteristics, hardness and water resistance within one resin, thereby
securing an overall practical compromise better than that
obtainable by any other class of resins.

The chemical and physical nature of rosin-modified phenol

resins is not easily understood and, therefore, a number of mistaken ideas continue to circulate about their composition and properties. For instance, the fact that their major component is rosin, has led to the erroneous conception that they are nothing but rosin-extended, in other words, let down pure phenolics. Unfortunately, the literature on the subject is often vague and contradictory, possibly dominated by economic factors.

The following comments will enable the practical user of resins to

form his own unbiased opinion

on the merits of rosin modified phenolics. The comments are based on a few relatively simple determinations, and are substantiated by the rules on the reactive capacities of phenolic and alcoholic hydroxyl groups in phenol formaldehyde condensates, which have been previously discussed.

The chemical changes which occur during the first step of producing rosin-modified phenolics were demonstrated by heating rosin with a given amount of pure phenolic, and determining the acid values and melting points of the mixture after certain periods of time. It seemed desirable to include in these tests the determination of acetyl values, assuming that they indicate the hydroxyl values of the modified phenolics. However, true hydroxyl values could not be obtained in this way because rosin alone, when treated with acetic anhydride, yields acetyl values of considerable magnitude.

The experiments were carried out by heating gum rosin with three types of pure phenol resins, *i.e.* an acid-condensed para tertiary amyl phenol resins of an acid value of 80 and a melting point of 95° C., an alkali-condensed para tertiary amyl phenol resin of an acid value of 55 and a melting point of 70° C., and an alkali-condensed, highly viscous, bis phenol resin of an acid value of 50. In all cases the rosin was fused together with 25% of the resin at about 110° C., heated to 270° C., and held at this temperature for two hours. Samples for acid value titration and determination of melting points were taken at the beginning and the end of the experiment. A blank test was carried out with rosin alone, showing that rosin lost 20 units of its acidity under the conditions of this test.

The acid values determined for the rosin combinations with pure phenol resins are summarized in *Table 6*.

Table 6.   Acid Values of Rosin Phenol Resin Combinations.

	Acid Values of Rosin Combined with 25% of		
	Acid-condensed Amyl Phenol Resin	*Alkali-condensed Amyl Phenol Resin*	*Alkali-condensed Bis Phenol Resin*
Sample taken at 110° C.	148	143	142
Sample taken after 2 hours at 270° C.	132	127	126
Change in acidity of rosin portion alone	16	16	16
Change in acidity of rosin phenolic combination	0	0	0

Table 6 demonstrates the complete lack of reactivity between rosin and the phenolic bodies. The condensates of the alkyl-substituted phenols, and of the bis phenol, did not lose any of their alkali titration when heated with rosin. The small decrease in acid value determined at 270° C., for the rosin phenolic combinations is identical with the drop in acid value undergone by the rosin portion alone.

The melting point values determined for the rosin combinations with pure phenol resins are summarized in *Table 7*.

As the table shows, acid-condensed resins do not cause any increase in melting points, nor is any foaming observed. Increases in viscosities are slight. Alkali-condensed resins induce strong increases in melting points, the bis phenol condensate being more efficient in this respect than the alkylphenol condensate. Corresponding determinations of vis-

Table 7. Melting Points of Rosin Phenol Resin Combinations

Melting Points of Rosin Combined with 25% of	Sample Taken at 110° C.	Sample Taken at 270° C.	Change	Performance on Heating
Acid-condensed amyl phenol resin	83° C.	83° C.	0	No foam
Alkali-condensed amyl phenol resin	78° C.	130° C.	52° C.	Heavy Foam
Alkali-condensed bis phenol resin	73° C.	146° C.	73° C.	Heavy Foam

cosities indicate that alkali-condensed pure phenol resins raise viscosities in the same pronounced manner as they raise the melting points. Such increases are accompanied by heavy foaming of the mixture.

From the facts given in *Tables 6* and *7*

some interesting conclusions

can be drawn. Acid-condensed phenol bodies are unsuitable for modified phenolics, because they do not improve the hardness and the viscosity of the resin to a sufficient extent. Acid-condensed phenolics, however, may have merits as additions in certain modified phenolics, where a large amount of free alcoholic hydroxyl groups is required, for instance, for especially high reactivity with acidic oils.

Alkali-condensed phenol bodies make the ideal materials for modified phenolics, because they impart hardness and viscosity to the resin compound, and do not lose the reactivity of their phenolic and alcoholic hydroxyl groups. As has been pointed out, all of the phenolic hydroxyl groups initially added to the rosin by way of the resinified condensate are still present in the finished modified phenol resins and do not disappear even when the resins are subjected to continued treatment for a long time, as in the maturing process. The presence of free phenolic hydroxyl groups can be shown analytically by the alkali-fusion method, through which free phenol can be isolated and identified.

The alcoholic hydroxyl groups, on the other hand, are reduced in number, as previously explained, during heat treatment, to the extent that only about one-third of their initial quantity is still left free and reactive in the finished modified phenolic. This amount is large enough to convey to the resin substantial reactivity with fatty acids. It is important to note that the decrease in free alcoholic hydroxyl groups is not due to a reaction with rosin, but simply to a self-condensation of the phenolic body which, at the same time, produces increased hardness and viscosity.

Since no chemical reaction between rosin and phenol condensate takes place in the manufacture of modified phenolic resins, these resins have to be considered as solutions or

dispersions of the phenolic bodies

in the resin component. The advantage of this condition lies in the fact that the hydroxyl groups of the phenol condensate are able to enter into chemical reactions, when the modified phenolics are cooked with oils in the varnish-making process. Their phenolic hydroxyls are of the oil-reactive type, characteristic of alkali-condensed phenolics and, therefore, are capable of entering into the fatty chain of the oil molecule. Their alcoholic hydroxyls link up by esterification with the fatty acids initially present in the oil or formed during the heating of the oil. The final heat combination of modified phenol resins with oil in this way becomes so intimate that phenols can no longer be liberated when fused with alkali.

A further improvement of rosin-modified phenol resins has been achieved by the introduction of new types of phenol compounds with the

characteristics of an ether.

They possess the normal phenolic and alcoholic hydroxyl groups, which do not react with rosin and remain free in modified phenolics, but in addition contain a certain number of hydroxyls, which are able to link up with abietic-type acids. Details of the improved procedure are described in the Author's U.S. patents Nos. 2,268,946 and 2,268,947. The phenol-modified ethers, essential to the process, are formed by a peculiar reaction between phenol alcohols and glycerine, which is predicated on certain limiting conditions. Useful for the production of phenol ethers are the dialcohols of para tertiary amyl and butyl phenols, provided they are in a mono-molecular state, as obtained by carrying out the alkaline condensation process at low temperatures, and arresting it at the very moment at which the formaldehyde is practically absorbed by the phenol. They are obtained in the form of thin, oily liquids, and have the tendency to crystallize from their benzol solution in the form of white needles. To convert the monomolecular phenol dialcohol into the phenol ether, it is mixed with anhydrous glycerine, and the homogeneous mixture is subjected to vacuum treatment at room temperature, for instance, at a vacuum of at least 10-20 mm at temperatures of 15-25° C. Under such conditions the ether forming reaction proceeds vividly with heavy foaming. Water is split off during the reaction, but no phenolic decomposition products are distilled off. The reaction depends mainly on sufficiently high vacuum, for if the vacuum is decreased below a certain limit, the reactivity drops suddenly and can be promoted only by further slight increase in temperature. However, temperatures which favor self-condensation must be strictly avoided.

The monomeric phenol dialcohols react with glycerine in equimolecular ratios, as brought out by a series of tests. A determination of the amount of water split off during the reaction, indicates that as a rule the two alcoholic hydroxyl groups of the phenol dialcohol link up with two hydroxyl groups of the glycerine, thereby forming compounds of ether-like character, and at the same time leaving

one glycerine hydroxyl group

in the whole complex free for esterification with rosin. The latter factor is the most essential feature of the process, because it allows the chemical linkage of the phenol condensate with the rosin component in the production of rosin-modified phenol resins. The advantage is obvious. In ordinary modified phenol resins the pure phenolic component is present in the form of a physical dispersion within the surrounding medium and, therefore, in cooking the resin with oil, the oil is chemically combined only with the phenolic and not with the rosin component. If, however, the two components of the modified phenolic are linked together chemically, the combination of resin and oil during varnish cooking becomes complete, because all three components, *i.e.*, the phenolic body, the rosin compound and the oily component are bound together chemically. Due to the higher complexity of the compound, a varnish of improved protective characteristics is obtained.

The molecular weights of

normal rosin-modified phenolics

vary between 1200 and 1400. For instance, a modified bis phenol resin of a melting point of 145° C. has a molecular weight of 1200; a resin of the same type, more viscous and with a melting point of 155° C., shows a value of 1375. The resinified phenolic condensate itself, present in these modified resins, is probably in a state of agglomeration in which 6 or 7 single molecules are united into one group. On further prolonged heating they are possibly enlarged into molecules consisting of 7 or 8 monomeric units.

Non-esterified modified phenolics average molecular weights of 1100-1200, *i.e.* have relatively low values. Esterification of such resins does not increase the molecular size to the extent that could be expected theoretically, demonstrating again that structural resin chemistry is highly complicated.

In accordance with the experience that protective characteristics of a resin improve as a rule with its molecular size, manufacturing procedures are directed to obtaining large molecular weights. Molecular weights of rosin-modified phenolics can be increased by overloading them with phenolic condensates and high molecular alcohols. In both cases, however, the resins acquire a pronounced tendency to become gelatinous and insoluble.

Molecular enlargement is carried out in a much safer and more advantageous way by subjecting the resins to the

maturing process

the scientific principles and technical achievements of which have been described generally in a previous chapter.

To demonstrate in detail the interesting phenomena connected with the maturing process, the following concrete case is cited. It deals with a glycerine-esterified rosin-modified phenolic, containing 18% of a bis phenol-formaldehyde condensate, and having a molecular weight of 1250. After being subjected to a 20-hour vacuum treatment at 260° C., its molecular weight is 1800, *i.e.* the molecular association has increased by 550 units.

The agglomeration is accompanied by a substantial

improvement in the technical properties

of the resin, details of which are recorded in *Table 8*, describing the change of phenolic resin properties during the maturing process.

Table 8 shows that the melting point increases noticeably with the molecular weight, whereas the viscosity remains practically unchanged. The solubility of the resin is nearly doubled by the agglomeration procedure. The values given are the number of c.c. of mineral spirits which cause cloud

Table 8.　Change of Resin Constants During Maturing of a Phenolic

Resin Property	*Characteristic Expressed As*	*Resin Constants* Before Maturing	After
Molecular Size	Molecular weight	1250	1800
Hardness	Melting point	150° C.	165° C.
Viscosity	Gardner scale letter	Z_1-Z_2	Z_1-Z_2
Solubility	Titration value	15 c.c.	25 c.c.
Chemical resistance	Acid value	25	10
	Iodine value	120	80
	Portion saponified after 3 hours	100%	70%
Heat stability	Heating loss	1.5%	0.5%

formation, when added slowly to a solution of 6 grams of resin in 4 grams of xylol.

With the growth of molecular size, the acid value drops to the level which is practically equivalent to the quantity of the phenol body used for modification, indicating at the same time nearly complete neutralization of the rosin part, and resulting in improved chemical resistance.

The iodine value shows a decided drop from 120, for the non-agglomerated resin, to 80 for the high molecular resin. This decrease is caused by internal linkages occurring during the procedure, which eliminate oxidizable points and other sensitive spots in the resin molecule, with the practical result of more stable and more durable products.

Chemical stability is well expressed by the speed with which resins can be saponified. Non-matured phenol resins, as such, have great resistance to saponification, but this resistance is increased further by building up the molecular size, as appears from *Table 8*. The comparative tests reported in the table are made by refluxing the two resin samples dissolved in toluol, under equal conditions, with an excess of potassium hydroxide dissolved in butanol, and determining by titration after three hours of boiling, the portion of the resin that is saponified.

The heat·stability of the low molecular sample is poorer than that of the high molecular resin; the last named loses only one-third of the weight lost by the former on heating, all conditions being equal.

Rosin-modified phenolics may vary largely in their specific properties due to

variations in the type and relative amount

of their components. For surface coatings and printing inks, alkyl-substituted and bis phenol modified resins are under consideration in this book. The former are distinguished by good solubility and resistance, the latter by hardness, viscosity and outstanding drying characteristics. As a rule, the resins are esterified with glycerine. Pentaerythritol imparts particularly high water and alkali resistance, and produces heat stability. To obtain special characteristics, the rosin part may be left unesterified, in which case a particularly high amount of phenolic body can be introduced. When superior color stability is wanted, the phenolics are combined with maleic or fumaric resins in various ways and quantities. Another possibility for variation is based on changing the rosin component by the use of gum rosin, wood rosin, polymerized or hydrogenated rosin.

Specific questions concerning individual resins in this field are discussed under the heading of "The Applications of Resins."

Ever since rosin-modified phenolics came into existence, *i.e.* for more than twenty years, they have been suspected of being nothing more than glorified ester gums. The previous comments have shown how erroneous such an assumption is, and accordingly, rosin-modified phenolics not only have maintained their position over the years, but have continued to grow in quantity of consumption and diversification of practical uses, and this increase has taken place in spite of the advent of many new and useful classes of resins.

Chapter III

Maleic Resins

Next to the rosin-modified phenolic resins, the group of rosin-modified maleic resins is of importance to the manufacture of surface coatings and printing inks, and within the class of surface coatings, is of particular value for nitrocellulose lacquers. Due to the constantly growing volume of their production and the continuously extending field of application, a great deal of empirical knowledge has been collected as to the formation and reactivity of maleic resins. In spite of this development, the primary chemical conceptions governing maleic resins have remained comparatively vague, and it is, therefore, the object of the technological study in this chapter to furnish more basic information, through new facts and figures, which may serve to contribute to a clearer understanding of the chemistry of maleic resins. Facts and figures refer to the reactivities of the polybasic acid components of the resins, and cover the characteristics of the large variety of finished maleic resins.

THE POLYBASIC ACID COMPONENTS

Among the three classes of ingredients which form maleic resins, *i.e.* the rosin-type materials, the polyhydric alcohols and the maleic-type polybasic acids, the group of polybasic acid components is the most important because this group has the greatest influence on the technical value of maleic resins. The class of acidic substances comprises maleic anhydride, maleic-acid, and fumaric acid.

For the majority of practical purposes,

maleic anhydride

is used as the polybasic acid component. It melts at 55-60° C., and distills at about 200° C., without decomposition. The degree of acidity which it shows on titration with alkali depends upon the solvent in which it is dissolved in the determination of its acid value. If it is dissolved in water, it converts quickly into maleic acid, and on neutralization with potassium hydroxide yields figures which are very close to the theoretical acid value of 1135. If maleic anhydride is dissolved in anhydrous alcohol or toluol, and titrated with alcoholic potassium hydroxide, an entirely different value is found. In the water-free solution, the maleic anhydride shows an acid value of only 530, *i.e.* less than half of that found in aqueous solution.

To explain this peculiarity, the presence of a mixed maleic acid-anhydride, formed by the association of two maleic acid radicals which are held together by an oxygen bridge, has been assumed. Such a compound has a molecular weight of 214 and would show an acid value of 530. The assumption of such a double molecule is supported by the fact that, in the field of organic chemistry, acid anhydrides are known to exist in dimolecular form, as has been proved by the example of dimethyl malonic acid anhydride.

As has been mentioned, maleic anhydride is easily converted from the anhydride into the acid when in aqueous solution. In the absence of water, however, it is very difficult to break down its anhydride-like structure, and it actually requires boiling with an excess of alcoholic potassium hydroxide to hydrolize the anhydride. If treated in this way, and if the unreacted portion of alkali is titrated back, alkali titration figures are obtained that are equivalent to the total acidity of the maleic anhydride converted into the dibasic maleic acid, *i.e.* equivalent to an acid value of 1135.

Maleic anhydride possesses two reactivities which are important for resin manufacture, *i.e.* the ability to esterify with polybasic alcohols, and the capacity to act chemically on rosin. The tendency to esterification is not very pronounced. For instance, the reaction with glycerine starts only at the comparatively high temperature of 180° C., and there is no heat developed during the period of esterification. As a rule, direct esterification between maleic anhydride and the polybasic alcohols, such as glycols, glycerine or pentaerythritols, does not often occur in the actual production of rosin-modified maleics, because in most practical procedures the maleic anhydride has an opportunity to act on rosin before esterification can begin.

The interaction between rosin and maleic anhydride is of a much more lively character than esterification. It starts at the very low temperature of 90° C., and is decidedly exothermic. At temperatures higher than 150° C., the reaction proceeds so violently, that a considerable temperature rise takes place, which has made maleic anhydride a dangerous substance in the hands of inexperienced operators, and which has been the cause of many a disastrous fire in resin kettles and plants.

The reaction between

rosin and maleic anhydride

leads to a chemical compound in which molecular equivalents of the two components are combined. This important fact appears from the determination of the melting points of a series of reaction mixtures, in which the relative amounts of the components were varied from 90 parts of rosin and 10 parts of maleic anhydride in steps of 10% change up to 10 parts of rosin and 90 parts of maleic anhydride. Gum rosin with a molecular weight of 520 was used, and in preparing the samples, care was taken that in all cases heating conditions were equal with regard to time and temperature. In addition, care was taken that the reaction was always carried to completion, which was achieved by holding the temperature of the reaction mixtures at 200° C., for 3 hours.

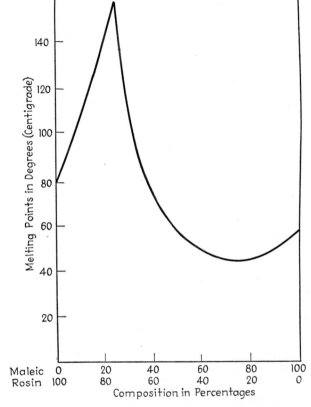

FIGURE 6. Melting points of rosin-maleic
anhydride combinations.

The melting points which were found for the systematically
changed combinations of rosin and maleic anhydride are
recorded in the graph of *Figure 6,* in which the relationship of

composition and melting points

is pictured in a very interesting curve. With increasing
additions of maleic anhydride to rosin, the melting point increases rapidly to a peak, which is located at a point equivalent
to a mixture of 75 parts of rosin and 25 parts of maleic anhydride. When more maleic anhydride is added, the melting

point drops even more rapidly than it had risen. After reaching a composition of about equal parts of rosin and maleic anhydride, the melting point curve flattens out, drops to a minimum point, which is slightly lower than the melting point of the pure maleic anhydride, and then rises gradually to this point.

Generally speaking, the melting points of chemical compounds are depressed by the additions of foreign substances. In this case, the melting point of the chemical compound formed by rosin and maleic anhydride is lowered by the addition of either rosin or maleic anhydride as such, and the peak of the curve indicates the composition of the chemical combination. Its location shows that rosin and maleic anhydride combine chemically at the ratio of 75 to 25, which is practically the proportion of the molecular weights of 302 for abietic acid and of 98 for maleic anhydride. As it appears from the molecular weight of the gum rosin used, a large part of the rosin is present in the form of double molecules. To account for equimolecular ratios, it is therefore reasonable to assume that a large part of the maleic anhydride also is present in dimolecular condition, possibly in the form of the previously mentioned double molecular acid anhydride. This assumption is supported by the fact that the molecular weight of the combination, possessing the maximum melting point, amounts to 650-700. With time and temperature of heating, it increases to nearly 800, which is the value for the straight dimolecular compound.

The reaction between three parts of rosin and one part of maleic anhydride leads to a uniform chemical compound, in short called

rosin-maleic acid.

Theorizing on its possible constitution and structural formula is without real object, because the rosin used is of undefined composition, containing a great number of different isomers of abietic acid, furthermore, pimaric and possibly other acids.

The reaction between rosin and maleic anhydride does not start at temperatures below 90° C., even in the presence of common solvents. If enough solvent is present to keep the reaction mixture liquid, the two substances begin to react with each other distinctly, developing heat, at a temperature of 90-92° C. The reaction progresses slowly at temperatures of about 100° C., but the reaction speed increases quickly with rising temperatures. At 140-160° C., several hours, and at 180-200° C., only one to two hours, are required to complete the chemical combination of the two ingredients. A definite end point is reached in all cases, indicated by the fact that, on continued heating, the acid value remains constant.

When rosin and maleic anhydride combine chemically, a reaction loss of 4-5% in weight occurs, a figure that is evidenced by both laboratory experiment and production experience. The escaping material consists mostly of water and also contains carbon dioxide and volatile low molecular acids. The formation of such reaction products is probably due to the fact that some of the highly oxidizable hydrogen atoms of the abietic type acids, which are characteristic of them, have acted on the maleic group.

The material loss, amounting to 500-1000 pounds in normal production batches of 10,000 to 20,000 pounds is substantial, and is about equivalent to one molecule of water escaping from the reaction of one molecule of the rosin acid with one molecule of maleic anhydride. This large loss in weight is incontestable evidence of the fact that the reaction between the two ingredients is

not of additive character.

This fact is disregarded in patent and scientific literature, both of which are dominated by the tendency to establish the diene reaction as the base for the rosin-maleic reaction. According to this theory, the maleic anhydride links up

directly with the conjugated double bonds which are assumed
to be present in rosin, and in this manner a completely closed
ring is formed by means of a plain additive reaction, which is
not accompanied by any splitting off of water or carbon
dioxide, and which causes no loss of material. In view of the
large loss actually sustained, it is difficult to accept the diene
mechanism as an explanation for the interaction between the
two ingredients generally, though a diene reaction might
occur on a small scale with some particular types of the rosin
acids present.

The acid value of the chemical compound of rosin and
maleic anhydride is found to be 270, which is identical with
the calculated figure, basing the calculation on acid value
of about 180 for the rosin and 530 for the maleic component present. The titration leads to a definite and pronounced end point, when the usual method of acid value
determination is used, *i.e.* when the material is dissolved in
toluol, and slowly neutralized with $10N$ alcoholic potassium
hydroxide. The potassium salt obtained in this way, if carefully acidified, gives back the original acid compound.

No definite end point of alkali action is found if the resinous
compound is

refluxed with an excess of potassium hydroxide

and the unreacted portion of the alkali is determined by back
titration. The figures obtained are larger than those found
by simple neutralization. They are not well defined, and vary
with the time and temperature of the alkali treatment. The
longer the refluxing is continued, the higher the values rise,
and refluxing in butanol solution, for instance, yields higher
figures than boiling in ethyl alcohol. Refluxing with alkali
dissolved in Carbitol yields particularly high values. When
the soap solutions obtained by refluxing are acidified, the
originally present substances are only partially recovered,
because the alkali has entered into reactions which go beyond

the neutralization of carboxyl groups and beyond the conversion of anhydride into acid groups.

The rosin-maleic compound has a comparatively saturated character, as appears from the low iodine value of 65, being even lower than that of hydrogenated rosin, which is about 80. Iodine values in general are good indicators of the degree of saturation; they drop decidedly when rosin is combined with maleic anhydride, amounting to 150 for pure gum rosin, being lowered to 105 by combination with 10% maleic anhydride, and to 70 by combining it with 30% maleic anhydride. The saturated character of the rosin maleic compound is possibly due to a direct attachment of the double bond of the maleic anhydride to the active bond in the rosin acids, whereby those two important points of unsaturation satisfy each other. This assumption is well supported by the fact that maleic anhydride does not react with hydrogenated rosin, which has lost its active double bond by the addition of hydrogen.

The rosin maleic compound, made by fusion of equimolecular quantities, has a melting point of 140° C. It is heat stable up to temperatures of about 225° C. If heated alone considerably beyond 250° C., its color begins to darken, its melting point decreases, and its iodine value drops from 65 to nearly half this value, whereas the acid values hardly change. If heated with glycerine it starts to react by esterification at 225° C., forming a quickly gelatinizing resin. Using, for instance, 20% glycerine and an esterification temperature of 260° C., the resin converts into an insoluble and infusible mass after five hours of heating.

If the rosin-maleic acid is

heated with neutral drying oils

it enters into chemical reactions, evidenced by decreasing acid values of such combinations. For instance, if two parts of linseed oil of an acid value of 2.5 are heated for two hours at 260° C. with one part of the rosin-maleic compound under discussion, with an acid value of 270, the resulting reaction product has an acidity of only 48 as compared to the arithmetical mean of 92.

The rosin-maleic compound is insoluble in mineral spirits, and soluble in coal tar solvents. It has the peculiarity of being miscible with diethylene glycol and is distinguished by complete solubility in low molecular alcohols, *i.e.* methyl, ethyl, isopropyl and butyl alcohol. The glycol and ethyl alcohol solutions have the peculiarity of tolerating substantial amounts of water additions without precipitation of resin. For instance, the alcohols may contain up to 25% by weight of water and still be able to keep the rosin-maleic compound in solution.

All alcoholic solutions are stable on storage, except the solution in ethyl alcohol, which on standing forms a white crystalline precipitate. The white crystals are identified by combustion analysis and molecular weight determination as

the monomolecular reaction product

of rosin and maleic anhydride, *i.e.* the monomeric rosin-maleic acid, which is later described in detail.

The speed of crystallization increases with the concentration of the alcohol solution, *i.e.* a 50% solution may form crystals over night, whereas a 25% solution may require one to two weeks. This speed is also pronouncedly accelerated by the action of light, but is not influenced by low temperature, water content of the alcohol, additions of crystal nuclei or mineral acids such as hydrochloric acid.

The total quantity of the white precipitate, weighed after washing and drying, amounts to 35-40% of the total weight of rosin maleic compound, originally present in the solution. A quantity of 30 to 33% precipitates quickly, and the balance crystallizes slowly over a period of several weeks, after which time the solution is free from crystallizable parts. Investigation shows that the resin finally remaining in alcohol solution has an acid value of about 200 and a melting point of 140° C. The solution, therefore, suggests itself as a very suitable substitute for shellac solutions.

The yield of the crystalline rosin-maleic reaction product, in short called

rosin-maleic acid

obtained from the ethyl alcohol solution, declines when the temperature at which the two ingredients are reacted is increased. Suitable reaction temperatures lie between 160° and 220° C., the best temperature range for practical purposes being 180-200° C. The yield from gum rosin is slightly higher than that from wood rosin. Polymerized rosin is restricted in its reactivity with maleic anhydride and hydrogenated rosin does not react at all. The two last named rosin types, therefore, are unsuitable for preparing the rosin-maleic acid.

To obtain the white crystals in pure form they are filtered off, washed with alcohol, and dried at 110° C. for 24 hours. The last traces of alcohol remain very firmly and are completely removed only by fusing the crystals.

The acid value of the crystalline acid can be determined by neutralization with $10N$ alcoholic potassium hydroxide in toluol solution at room temperature, and is found to be 280. This value is definite and reproducible and indicates the number of free carboxyl groups.

Higher values are obtained when the acid is refluxed with an excess of alkali and the unused portion of the alkali is titrated back. It is reasonable to assume that the figures, found in this manner, may be indicative of the presence of anhydrides, lactones or other saponifiable matter. The actually determined figures increase decidedly with the time and the temperature of the alkali treatment of the crystals, without reaching a constant and reproducible value and, therefore, are unsuitable for the drawing of any quantitative chemical conclusions.

The molecular weight of the crystals, determined by the freezing point depression of diphenylamine, is found to be 380-400. This value establishes the important fact that the crystalline substance represents the rosin-maleic acid, under discussion, in its monomolecular form. The monomeric acid is already partially present in the fused reaction product, as shown by the latter's molecular weight, but more monomeric material is formed while the resin is in ethyl alcohol solution.

By relating molecular weight to acid value, the

basicity of the rosin-maleic acid

can be determined according to the rule that the basicity equals

$$\frac{\text{Molecular Weight} \times \text{Acid Value}}{56000}$$

Inserting the two figures previously given, *i.e.* 400 for the molecular weight and 280 for the acid value, it follows that the rosin-maleic acid is a dibasic acid, *i.e.* contains two carboxyl groups. In addition to the two carboxyls, anhydride groups are present, as indicated by the behavior of the crystals when boiled with an excess of alkali.

The monomeric rosin-maleic acid crystals are insoluble in aliphatic and aromatic hydrocarbons, in low and high molecular alcohols and other organic solvents at room temperature. On heating they dissolve and on cooling they recrystallize. The crystalline acid does not show any positive Lieberman-Storch reaction, indicating the absence of even traces of rosin.

The melting point of the material is found to be 225° C., *i.e.* extremely high and higher than the melting point of any other polybasic acid used in resin manufacture. The melting point is very sharp and fusing at the melting point occurs without decomposition. If heated more than 20° C. beyond the melting point, the monomeric compound starts to polymerize into the dimolecular product, as shown by the increase in molecular weight, which gradually goes up from 400 to 800. Dimerization is completed after several hours' heating at 280° C.

The melting point of the polymerized rosin-maleic acid is about 75° C. lower than that of the monomeric acid. Therefore, during the conversion period, the peculiar phenomenon of a double melting point is observed in the usual mercury or A.S.T.M. method, in which the amorphous dimolecular phase starts to move long before the crystalline monomeric phase melts.

The amorphous rosin-maleic acid obtained from the monomeric product is soluble in alcohol and aromatic hydrocarbons. It is darker in color than the crystalline acid, contains a certain amount of rosin due to decomposition, as indicated by a positive Lieberman-Storch reaction, and otherwise behaves like the rosin-maleic compound produced by fusing together equimolecular quantities of the two ingredients.

The monomeric rosin-maleic acid can be esterified with diethylene glycol and glycerine by fusing the ingredients gently at temperatures which are a few degrees above 225° C. and then heating the mixture to the temperature of esterification.

Ester formation with glycerine

occurs with slow speed at 240° to 250° C., and is carried out in practice at 260° to 270° C. Esterification with pentaerythritol does not yield the monomeric ester because polymerization of the acid takes place before ester formation begins.

The glycerine esters of the monomeric rosin-maleic acid have unique properties which in many ways are different from those of the polymerized acid. They are fusible without gelling, heat hardening, charring or decomposition; they possess extremely high melting points of 180-200° C. and higher, depending upon the degree of neutralization. An ester of an acid value of about 100, for instance, possesses a melting point of 195° C. The amount of glycerine may vary from 15-25%. If smaller amounts of glycerine are used, the rosin-maleic acid is not esterified quickly enough to avoid polymerization and decomposition; if higher amounts are employed, the esterified product contains mono- and diglycerides. Both conditions tend to lower the melting point of the resinous ester.

Equivalent esters of the dimolecular rosin-maleic acid cannot be produced because, when esterification is attempted, the reaction mixture gelatinizes into an infusible and insoluble mass, as soon as a melting point of 155° C. is reached.

The reason for the

vastly different behavior

of the monomeric and the dimolecular ester is probably to be found in the great difference in the size of their molecules. A simple calculation shows that the ester of the monomeric acid should possess a molecular weight of about 1300, which is entirely in the field of soluble and fusible resins, whereas the dimeric acid should have a molecular weight of about 2500, *i.e.* a size which is far beyond the deadline of 2000, beyond which resins become insoluble and infusible.

The glycerine esters of the monomeric rosin maleic acid are soluble in coal tar solvents, giving solutions which are homogeneous in appearance and free from overpolymerized particles, a 60% xylol solution yielding a viscosity of about Z_5 to Z_6 on the Gardner scale. The resins are also miscible with, and soluble in, all rosin-based resinous esters, at temperatures of 225°-250° C. They can be dissolved, for instance, in rosin glycerine or pentaerythritol esters and in rosin-modified maleics or phenolics, improving their melting point and viscosity. They also dissolve in fused natural copals, copal-type synthetic resins and other copal based resinous esters, rendering the combined product harder and more viscous.

The exceptionally hard glycerine esters of the rosin-maleic acid are insoluble in drying oils even at high temperatures. They can be combined with the oil only by protracted heat treatment, during which structural changes in both the resinous and the oily phase take place.

The reactivity of rosin with maleic anhydride is elucidated further by a study of the chemical reactions that occur between

rosin and maleic acid

itself. Maleic acid has a melting point of 135° C., and starts to boil at 160° C., accompanied by decomposition into maleic anhydride and water. Its acid value, in alcohol toluol mixture, is found to be 965, in accordance with the theoretical acidity, but quite in contrast to the behavior of maleic anhydride.

Maleic acid starts to react with rosin at the low temperature of 110° C., its reaction speed increasing with rising temperature. The reaction, differing from that of maleic anhydride, which is exothermic, proceeds without the development of heat. A study of the melting points of the reaction products of rosin and maleic acid in changing ratios shows that the highest melting point is reached when the ingredients are combined in equimolecular ratios, indicating that at this point a uniform chemical compound is formed.

This compound is identical with the product obtained from rosin and maleic anhydride and also crystallizes in monomeric form from the solution in ethyl alcohol. The monomolecular substance has a molecular weight of 400, an acid value of 280 and a melting point of 225° C. Relating acid value and molecular weight, it follows that only two carboxyl groups are present per molecule, indicating that the reaction between the rosin acids and maleic acid, which forms the white monomeric precipitate in ethyl alcohol solutions, is not a plain addition which occurs in the Diels-Alder mechanism. An additive reaction necessarily leads to a substance with three carboxyl groups and does not cause one carboxyl group to vanish.

Another dibasic acid of the maleic type, which is of importance for the production of rosin-modified maleic resins, is the

fumaric acid.

Fumaric acid does not melt, but sublimes at about 205° C. At slightly higher temperatures, if heated alone, it decomposes into maleic anhydride and water, splitting off also carbon dioxide and acetic acid in minor side reactions. Chemically speaking, fumaric acid is the "trans" isomer of the maleic acid and, therefore, possesses a structure which, due to steric hindrances, leads to reactions that are slower in speed and different in character, when compared with maleic reactions.

The reduced reactivity of fumaric acid with rosin appears from the fact that this reaction, which in itself is only very slightly exothermic, starts only at 185° C., *i.e.* at a temperature which is nearly 100° C. higher than that at which maleic anhydride or acid begin to react with rosin. The reduced reactivity of fumaric acid also appears from its great reluctance to enter into a reaction with polymerized rosin.

The different

character of the rosin fumaric acid reaction product

appears from a comparison of the acid values, the melting points, the viscosities and the solubilities of the equivalent fumaric and maleic rosin compounds.

The acid values of rosin fumaric acid combinations, prepared at about 200° C., are practically identical with the arithmetical mean of the acid values of the two components according to their relative ratio, evidencing the fact that no carboxyl group is eliminated, as in the case of the rosin maleic combination. Obviously the fumaric acid, quite different from the maleic compound, forms a tribasic acid with rosin, which probably favors the formation of more complex three-dimensional structures in fumaric resins, rendering them harder and more viscous. This assumption is supported by the fact that fumaric resins generally have higher molecular weights than maleic resins.

When the rosin fumaric acid combinations are heated beyond 240° C., their acid values decrease; but there is no evidence that this decrease is due to a conversion of the fumaric into the maleic component.

The melting point of rosin fumaric acid reaction mixtures, made at 200° C., increases with the amount of fumaric acid added, until nearly equimolecular quantities are combined. The melting points of rosin fumaric acid reaction mixtures are about 25° C. higher than those containing the same amount of maleic acid. On heating beyond 240° C., the reaction mixtures decrease in melting point down to the level of the corresponding maleic compounds. This change, however, does not take place in the presence of glycerine, which esterifies the carboxyl groups and obviously protects the sensitive structure of the tribasic acid.

In accordance with the observations made on melting points, the viscosities of rosin fumaric acid combinations are higher than those of the corresponding maleic compounds. The

differences are very substantial;

for instance, a combination of 100 parts of rosin with 25 parts of fumaric acid has a viscosity of Z_2 in 60% xylol solution on the Gardner scale, compared to a viscosity of K for the equivalent maleic acid compound. If heated alone the viscosity of the fumaric compound drops to the level of the maleic compound. If the rosin fumaric acid combination is esterified, its viscosity remains considerably above the viscosity of the equivalent esterified maleic compound.

The rosin fumaric acid possesses the same solubility in

organic solvents as the rosin-maleic reaction product; however, it differs in the performance of its ethyl alcohol solution. This solution is stable on storage and does not precipitate any monomeric crystals of rosin-fumaric acid on standing.

In addition to fumaric acid and maleic acid products, only

the malic acid

has been suggested for producing the maleic-type resins. Malic acid is a hydroxy succinic acid which supposedly breaks up mainly into fumaric acid and a small amount of maleic anhydride at temperatures between 160° and 200° C. Rosin malic combinations made at temperatures of about 200° C., have properties which lie in between the properties of products obtained from either fumaric acid or maleic anhydride. The same is true for the rosin-malic acid products obtained by esterification with polybasic alcohols at temperatures of 260°-270° C.

Other polybasic acids, in particular those which are used in the manufacture of alkyd resins, are unsuitable for the production of maleic-type resins. These

acidic substances

which include phthalic anhydride, succinic acid, sebacic and adipic acids, do not enter into a chemical reaction with rosin. Though they can be combined with rosin by joint esterification to form a homogeneous mixed ester-resin, their combination is only superficial. By saponification and acidification of the soap solution, the original acids can be regained. Quite different from maleic and fumaric acids, they do not lose their identity when they are processed with the rosin acids.

The same is true for citric and itaconic acids. Both these acids do not enter into a reaction with rosin, which increases the latter's melting point and, therefore, have no place in the manufacture of maleic resins.

THE VARIETIES OF MALEIC RESINS

In spite of the comparatively few resin-forming ingredients used to build up the rosin-modified maleics, a large variety of resins is not only theoretically possible but actually manufactured on a commercial scale. The possibilities for variation are manifold. The type of rosin, of dibasic acid and of polybasic alcohol may be varied; the sequence in which they react with each other may be changed; and the amounts and relative proportions of the ingredients may be altered in various ways. Another important possibility of varying resin characteristics is based on the maturing process.

The properties of the

rosin component

are conveyed to the rosin-modified maleic and, therefore, changes in this component, express themselves in the qualities of the final resin. To cite a few examples, gum rosin produces relatively high viscosity, wood rosin increases solubility, while polymerized rosin raises the melting point. The color of all rosin types is little changed by the resin-making procedure.

As explained in the previous chapter, the most important factor affecting the technical properties of the resins is the type of unsaturated dibasic acid used. While characteristics of the resins differ in finer points when maleic anhydride or maleic acid is being used, they show significant differences when fumaric acid is employed. Another possibility of varying resin properties consists in the use of several of the acid types simultaneously, a procedure that has proved successful in making tailor-made maleic resins for selected purposes.

In addition to the changes in rosin types and acid components, the

process of esterification

allows many modifications. In the extreme case, no esterification is carried out at all as, for example, with certain glycol-

soluble maleic resins; or, resins are neutralized only to a very
limited degree, as in the case of certain alcohol-soluble maleics.
The most important variable factor is the type of esterifying
alcohol, ranging from those with two hydroxyl groups up to
those with four or more hydroxyl groups, each imparting individual characteristics to the finished resin. The dibasic
alcohol of practical importance is the ethylene glycol. The
standard trihydric alcohol is glycerine. Sorbitol and mannitol
also act as trihydric alcohols, in spite of the fact that their
chemical formulae show six hydroxyl groups. Normal pentaerythritol is active with four hydroxyl groups, while the
ether alcohols of pentaerythritol, the so-called polypentaerythritols, may act with up to eight reactive hydroxyl groups
per molecule.

While resin characteristics depend largely on the type of
the ingredients used, they are little influenced by the sequence
in which the reactants are added and the order in which the
reactions follow each other. To prove this point, four maleic
resins of identical composition were prepared, using the same
conditions of time and temperature, changing the

sequence of the various resin-forming reactions.

In all cases an amount of 100 parts of gum rosin, 12 parts of
maleic anhydride and 18 parts of glycerine were used. In the
first sample the rosin was first reacted with maleic anhydride,
then the reaction product was esterified. The second sample
was prepared by treating the rosin with the total quantity of
glycerine and by reacting the glyceride thus obtained with
maleic anhydride. In the third sample the maleic anhydride
was dissolved in the total amount of glycerine, reacted with
it, and to the reaction product was added the rosin for esterification. The fourth sample was prepared by fusing all three
components together and reacting rosin, maleic anhydride
and glycerine with each other simultaneously.

The resulting four maleic resins were analyzed by determining the acid value, the melting point, the molecular weight, the viscosity and solubility, the last named two characteristics measured in the customary way by means of the Gardner scale and the mineral spirits titration. The figures obtained are reported in *Table 9.*

Table 9. Reaction Sequence and Resin Constants of Maleic Resins

Sequence of Reactions	*Acid Value*	*Melting Point*	*Viscosity*	*Solubility*	*Molecular Weight*
Rosin reacted with maleic anhydride, then esterified	22	141° C.	Q	29 c.c.	1350
Rosin esterified first, then treated with maleic anhydride	24	140° C.	O	26 c.c.	1300
Maleic anhydride esterified first, then reacted with rosin	20	143° C.	S	31 c.c.	1325
The three components of rosin, maleic anhydride, glycerine reacted together simultaneously	20	143° C.	T	27 c.c.	1400

The resin characteristics are very closely alike for all four resin samples and the differences do not exceed the limits of fluctuation to be expected in this type of technical experiment. The table, therefore, shows that no distinct relationship exists between the reaction sequence and the resin constants, and thereby indicates that in the resin forming process, the same mixed esters are finally produced,

regardless of the sequence

in which the components have reacted with each other.

An important possibility of varying resin properties is offered by changing the amounts and relative proportion of the three components. Increasing the amount of polyhydric alcohol leads to very neutral resins and to resins containing free hydroxyl groups, which impart to them the valuable ability to react chemically with oils. Increasing the amount of dibasic unsaturated acid promotes the hardness and viscosity of the resins and reduces their solubility and fusibility. If both polybasic acids and alcohols are increased, resins are obtained that show a strong tendency to gelatinize and are inhomogeneous, due to the presence of over-polymerized particles.

Another interesting method of changing property combinations in maleic resins is based on the application of

the maturing process

which has been described in a previous chapter. This unique process makes it possible, for instance, to unite in one resin high melting point with high solubility, two characteristics which, as a rule, are inversely proportional to each other. It also makes it possible to impart to maleic resins a degree of chemical resistance which they do not inherently possess.

Table 10. Change of Resin Constants During Maturing of a Maleic

Resin Property	Characteristic Expressed As	Resin Constants Before | After Maturing	
Molecular size	Molecular weight	1375	1950
Hardness	Melting point	150° C.	160° C.
Viscosity	Gardner scale letter	*Y-Z*	*Y-Z*
Solubility	Titration value	15 c.c.	80 c.c.
Chemical resistance	Acid value	30	15
	Iodine value	105	80
	Portion saponified after one and one-half hours	100%	80%
Heat stability	Heating loss	3%	1%

In view of the theoretical and practical importance of the maturing process, the case of a maleic resin with a melting point of 150° C., which was subjected to a 24 hour maturing at 255° C., is reported in *Table 10,* giving details on the changes in resin characteristics..

The molecular weight of the initial resin investigated was 1375. After the maturing treatment a molecular weight of 1950 was found, *i.e.* the molecular association had increased by 575 units. Together with the molecular size, the hardness of the resin, measured by the melting point, had increased from 150° to 160° C. At the same time the resin viscosity, measured by comparing a 60% resin solution in xylol with the standards of the Gardner scale, remained practically unchanged, in spite of the increase in the molecular association.

The solubility characteristics of the maleic resin under investigation were changed basically by the maturing process. The solubility was determined by titrating 10 grams of a solution of 60 parts of resin in 40 parts of xylol, with mineral spirits, until an incipient cloud appeared, and was expressed by the number of c.c. of mineral spirits used to reach this point. It showed a sudden rise from 15 c.c. to 80 c.c., *i.e.* the change was so great that the entire character of the resin was altered from the low to the high solubility type.

The chemical stability, reported in the table, was expressed in terms of the acid value, the iodine value and the speed of saponification. Acid and iodine values were measured in the ordinary way. For the determination of the speed of saponification, the resins were saponified in toluol-butanol solution measuring, after a given length of time, by back titration, the percentages of saponified material. The figures showed that the chemical resistance was improved considerably, as was to be expected, because the

molecular association

which accompanies maturing is based mainly on reactions occurring at sensitive points. The disappearance of chemically weak spots was particularly indicated by the decrease in acid value from 30 to 15, and by the drop in iodine value from 105 to 80.

Molecular association also has caused a distinct slowdown in the speed with which the resins were saponified. Only 85% of the high molecular, matured resin were saponified under conditions which would produce 100% saponification in low molecular, non-matured resins. The practical result was improved water and alkali resistance.

The table also shows that the heat stability had been improved, which is an important economic factor. The heating loss, undergone by the resin when heated for one hour at 285° C., had decreased from 3%, for the low molecular, to 1% for the high molecular resin.

To demonstrate the practical possibilities in

producing different varieties

of rosin-modified maleic resins with valuable property combinations, for a number of applications, the following typical examples are cited:

(1) *A quick-sanding resin of low viscosity, compatible with nitrocellulose and ethyl cellulose.*

(2) *An alcohol-soluble resin of high acid value suitable for high alcohol content finishes.*

(3) *A glycol-soluble, non-esterified resin to be used for steam-set inks.*

(4) *A high melting point resin, soluble in mineral spirits, useful for the modification of alkyd resins.*

(5) *A quick-bodying resin, insoluble in mineral spirits, designed for linseed or dehydrated castor oil varnishes.*

(6) *A high viscosity resin, soluble in hot oil, suitable for overprint varnishes and gloss inks.*

In addition to these examples of different maleic resins many other variations are possible as, for instance, through the modification with phenolic resins, which improves the water resistance of the combination.

Rosin-modified maleic resins show a few

chemical peculiarities

which are characteristic of them and which are important enough for a detailed discussion. They concern the determination of their acidity, questions of their saponification, and have reference to the chemical nature of the acids present in the resins.

When the acid value of maleic resins is taken in the customary way, the low point of a range is reached, in which the indicator turns red, but discolors quickly again on standing for several minutes. It is only after the upper point of this range is reached by adding more alkali, that the red indicator color no longer discolors, even on long standing. In one specific case, the first apparent end point seemed to indicate an acid value of 25, whereas the actual and final value was 35.

The peculiarly indefinite end point in alkali titrations is characteristic for maleic resins, and often helps in their identification. The phenomenon of

indefinite titration end points

is limited to esterified maleic resins. Non-esterified resins, in particular the pure rosin-maleic acid, yield sharp values. It is, therefore, probable that the latitude between the two points indicates the presence of a small amount, about 1%, of an easily saponifiable ester.

The saponification of maleic resins yields different values, depending upon the

temperature and the time of saponification

and the amount of alkali used, but to a lesser extent than previously reported for the pure rosin-maleic acid. Comparatively reproducible figures are obtained when 10 grams of resin, dissolved in toluol, are refluxed with 50 c.c. $1N$ butanol solution of potassium hydroxide for a period of six hours. The saponification figures obtained are higher than those caused by the saponification of the ester-like matter present, because the alkali not only saponifies esters, but also penetrates into the chemical structure of the resinous material.

Saponification values of ordinary maleic resins are high and, as a natural consequence, high speeds of saponification are observed. The rate of saponification for non-matured maleics is even higher than that of a good ester gum. For instance, refluxing the two resins with an excess of potassium hydroxide in butanol, under entirely equal conditions, it is found that after one hour 80% of the ester gum and 95% of the maleic resin have been saponified.

The acids liberated from maleic resins by saponification and acidification are partially oxidized rosin acids, and the rosin-maleic acid previously described. Free maleic acid cannot be reclaimed from the saponification liquids. Another dibasic acid instead is found after saponification, *i.e.*

succinic acid

which is obviously formed by the reducing action, at high temperature, of organic matter on the maleic radical.

Succinic acid is present in all rosin-modified maleic esters, and this interesting fact can be proved conclusively by identifying the succinic acid through its phenacyl ester. The last named ester can be obtained in its pure form from the resin in the following manner.

The resin sample is dissolved in toluol and saponified with a measured excess of $1N$ alcoholic potassium hydroxide. When the saponification is complete, the alkali is exactly neutralized by the addition of an equivalent amount of $1N$ aqueous sulfuric acid, which has previously been diluted with the same amount of water. Due to the addition of the mineral acid, the resinous acids are precipitated; they are filtered off and the aqueous filtrate is used for the further investigation. It contains the water-soluble acids, such as succinic, initially present in the resin.

The filtrate is concentrated on a water bath until dry and the residue is extracted, with a small amount of alcohol, in order to separate the organic acid from the potassium sulfate. The alcohol extract is diluted with alcohol, with the result that considerable amounts of crystals are separated out. They are filtered off, washed with alcohol and dried. For further purification these crystals are dissolved in water and heated with basic lead acetate solution just sufficient for their complete precipitation. The precipitate is filtered off, washed, suspended in water and freed from lead by treatment with hydrogen sulfide. The filtrate on evaporation yields the acid ready for identification. Its melting point is 180° C., *i.e.* that of succinic acid.

For further identification, the phenacyl ester of this acid is prepared in the customary way. Its melting point is found identical with that established for the chemically pure phenacyl succinic ester, *i.e.* 148° C. As a check, the two phenacyl esters, *i.e.* the one prepared from pure succinic acid, and the other one prepared from the acid isolated in the resin analysis, are mixed and the melting point of the mixture determined. The mixture melts sharply at the same temperature of 148° C.

As a rule, the amount of succinic acid found in maleic resins is small and seldom exceeds 2%. However, even this small amount is of the greatest

importance to the varnish maker.

Lead succinate, as well as cobalt succinate, are formed in maleic resin varnishes, when the two metals are added to the varnishes in the form of driers. Both lead and cobalt succinate possess little solubility in varnish solvents and, therefore, have a tendency to precipitate from varnishes, enamels, paints and ink vehicles. They may be held in pseudo solution for a few weeks by the surrounding colloidal matter, but finally precipitation occurs, with the result that the surface coating or printing ink material loses its drying properties.

The phenomenon of precipitation can be demonstrated spectacularly by adding a very small amount of an alcoholic solution of succinic acid to the intensely blue solution of cobalt naphthenate in mineral spirits. The deep blue of the cobalt solution is bleached instantaneously, due to the formation of insoluble cobalt succinate, which is precipitated and has a slightly pink color.

Rosin-modified maleic resins have been the

object of many criticisms

with regard to their technical value, mainly based on the contention that at best they can be considered as an improved ester gum. The first maleic resins were made commercially on a small scale about 1926, *i.e.* more than twenty years ago, and their practical importance for the coating and ink industries has grown continuously, their sales volume today equalling about that of modified phenolics. This upward development took place in spite of the many new resin types created during the same period, constituting good evidence of the inherent technical value of rosin-modified maleics. This is particularly true for the combination type of resins, which consist of rosin-modified maleics reinforced by phenol-formaldehyde bodies.

Chapter IV

Copal-type Synthetics

The technical merits of hard synthetic resins, especially of modified phenolics and maleics, as compared to natural gum copals, are obvious. Synthetic resins are produced under controlled conditions, yielding standardized properties and complying with detailed specifications. They are physically and chemically homogeneous throughout the batch, and uniform from batch to batch; they are brilliantly transparent in appearance, because they are free from colloidal or suspended foreign matter. Modified phenolics and maleics, as well as hard resin esters, are ready for immediate combination with oils, and when heat-processed in the varnish kettle they undergo only a nominal loss of weight.

Natural copals, on the other hand, are formed under a variety of conditions created by nature, and yield resins of indistinctly defined and fluctuating properties. In order to make them attain some degree of uniformity and meet certain specifications, they are graded and sorted by methods in which the human factor of error plays a predominant role.

As natural products

most of the copals contain water or aqueous solutions in various degrees of dispersion, and considerable quantities of foreign matter, such as sand, fragments of wood and bark, leaves and all kinds of organisms, especially insects. Gum copals are not ready for direct use in varnish making; for this purpose they have to be rendered oil-soluble by the cumbersome process of copal running. The production of large

129

quantities of run copal requires much time because it has to be carried out in small batches to avoid overfoaming. Gum running is a cracking process carried out at very high temperatures, which leads to a loss of material amounting to as much as 40%. The escaping decomposition products are practically worthless, thereby increasing the price of the fused copal by the percentage of weight loss. The high heat of fusing discolors the copal substance as such, and carbonizes the impurities with the result of intensely darkening the color of the melted product. The escaping vapors are obnoxious and dangerous for the workmen and are potential fire hazards.

In spite of these obvious drawbacks, the natural gums have retained a

remarkably strong position

in their fight against the synthetic resins because, according to practical experience, certain valuable properties are more pronounced in natural gums, after they have been depolymerized, than in synthetic resins. The old time varnish makers used to cite a number of advantages of copal varnishes over varnishes based on synthetics. According to them, all copal ester varnishes have higher viscosity, better bodying and drying properties, greater toughness and durability of the dried film, than rosin ester varnishes, all other conditions being equal. Compared to modified phenolics, copals are reputed to produce glossier varnishes with less tendency to blooming. Copals are also considered to cause better adhesion of varnishes, especially when the latter are baked on metal; and they have the well established reputation of producing varnishes which, when used as interior can coating, do not give off any unpleasant odor or bitter taste to aqueous liquids, such as beer or fruit juices, with which they come into contact. When copal varnishes are compared to maleic resin varnishes, it is admitted that their dried films are dark in the beginning, but it must be emphasized that they

FIGURE 7.   A copal-type synthetic.

soon bleach out; and it is stressed that copal varnishes, under otherwise equal conditions, are superior in rubbing and wearing characteristics.

The rivalry between natural gums and synthetic resins has given great impetus to research workers in both fields, with the result that knowledge gained on constitution and production of synthetic resins proved helpful in the chemistry and processing of copal gums, and vice versa. The natural opposition of the two classes, however, persisted until research developed a group of resins, which combine the advantages of both natural and synthetic resins, and eliminate many of their respective weaknesses. This new resin class, which is distinctly different from modified phenolics and maleics, is well characterized as the group of copal-type synthetics, because it combines the features of both natural and synthetic resins, emphasizing particularly the desirable features of the fossil gums. The most important copal-like property, as compared to the properties of orthodox synthetic resins of the same melting point and viscosity, is the high degree of solubility, molecular homogeneity, mechanical toughness and heat stability.

Figure 7 is the colored photograph of a

typical copal-type synthetic.

It is taken with incident light, originating from photo flood lights, which are reinforced by a series of reflectors. The inherent color beauty of this class of resin becomes particularly outstanding when the angle of incidence of the illuminating rays is about 45° relative to the plane of the object. The incident light, used in photographing the copal-type synthetic, produces distinct light reflexes at the many surfaces of fracture, covering the resin surface, which are characteristic of both natural fossil gums and copal-type synthetics.

The characterization of this new resin class as copal-type synthetics is well justified, furthermore, by the fact that the procedure of their manufacture is a combination of the methods used for the production of synthetic resins and the processing of natural gums.   The production of synthetic resins is based on polymerization, the processing of natural gums on depolymerization.   The carrying out of both procedures, one after the other, *i.e.* effecting first a molecular aggregation, which then is followed by molecular degradation, is the base for the production of copal-type synthetics.

For the purpose of building up

large molecular aggregates

in rosin-based synthetic resins, two methods are available. One method consists in the low temperature vacuum treatment of the maturing process, which has previously been described in detail.   The other method is the procedure used for the production of copal-type synthetic resins.   Quite different from the maturing process, it builds up large molecular aggregates from small units by incorporating into the rosin base comparatively large amounts of phenol-formaldehyde condensates, maleic type compounds, polyhydric alcohols or solubilized natural copals.   The amounts of such reactive additions have to be carefully adjusted.

If a certain quantity is exceeded, the product starts to gelatinize and usually converts into an infusible and insoluble mass during the course of a reaction, which is highly exothermic and difficult to control.   In this case the resulting product cannot be liquefied or solubilized again and, therefore, is fittingly called an irreversible gel.   Resin gels of this type are unsuitable for the production of copal-type synthetics.

For this purpose the additions have to be chosen in quality and quantity so that no infusible masses are formed, but that reversible gels are obtained, *i.e.* gelatinous resins, which can be reconverted into fusible and soluble materials by suitable methods.   In this process both polymerization and depolymerization are carried out in a systematic and controlled manner by proper selection of a specific resinous material, a special heating and cooling cycle and by the use of especially designed equipment and machinery. Because the entire procedure is unusual, it is worth while to elaborate on some of the factors of resin composition and manufacture, on which the new procedure is predicated.

The essential requirement as to chemical composition is the presence of

free hydroxyl groups

incorporated into the molecule in various ways. The simplest method of introducing hydroxyl groups, consists in using an excess of glycerine for resin making. The degelling effect of partial alcoholysis by means of glycerine is known from the experience that certain highly viscous alkyd or phenolic resins, when on the verge of gelatinization, can be reduced in viscosity, and that the agitator in the resin kettle can be kept moving, by the addition of glycerine. It is also known that maleic resins containing a high amount of maleic anhydride, with just enough glycerine to neutralize the acidity, tend to gelatinize into a rubber-like spongy mass, but can be prevented from complete gelation and liquefied again, by the addition of an excess of glycerine. Other polybasic alcohols exert a similar effect. Among them, the pentaerythritols occupy a special position, because highly condensed and polymerized rosin esters of the pentaerythritols have the peculiar property of acquiring exceptionally high viscosities before they actually gelatinize and before they stop the agitator in the kettle.

In the production of copal-type synthetics, a special class of pentaerythritol rosin esters has been found to be particularly suitable for the incorporation of hydroxyl groups and, therefore, has been made the object of extensive experimental and patent work in the Author's research laboratories. The particular group used for the purpose mentioned are resinified hydroxy esters of rosin acids with

pentaerythritol or polypentaerythritols

which are obtained by first alcoholizing normal pentaerythritol rosin esters by means of an excess of pentaerythritols,
and then resinifying under heat and vacuum the hydroxy
esters produced by the alcoholysis. The amount of polybasic
alcohol used is considerably higher than that required for
normal esterification and usually is adjusted so that at least
two hydroxyl groups in the molecule of the polyhydric alcohol
are left free.

The hydrolysis is directly comparable to the alcoholysis
practiced with other polyhydric alcohols, such as glycol, glycerine or those of a higher order. An interesting modification
of the hydrolysis is possible in the case of the polymers here
under consideration, by alcoholyzing the rosin ester with a
type of pentaerythritol different from that used for its esterification, for instance, employing the dipentaerythritol for
esterification and the normal pentaerythritol for alcoholysis.

The resinification of the hydroxy esters leads to clear, light
colored, oil-soluble resins, which are completely compatible
with other resins. Their most outstanding features, for the
purpose under discussion, is the fact that the major portion of
the free hydroxyl groups do not vanish during the resinification but remain available for further reactions.

The resinified hydroxy esters are distinguished by high
melting points and viscosities, by exceptional bodying speed
when cooked with soft oils such as linseed oil, and outstanding
film forming characteristics of such oil combinations, which
dry fast and hard. All these advantageous properties are
conveyed to resins, into which the resinified hydroxy esters
are incorporated.

A further possibility of introducing alcoholic hydroxyl
groups into the copal-type synthetics presents itself in the
use of

solubilized natural copals

which have been made soluble by the treatment of mastication, as described later in this chapter. If masticated natural gums are processed together with acidic rosin products or synthetic resins, they often act very similar to polyhydric alcohols, supplying good evidence that they contain free alcoholic hydroxyl groups. Literature also furnishes analytical evidence that hydroxyl groups are present in copals. According to the literature, the hydroxyl containing components can be isolated by selective precipitation of the copals; the hydroxy acids can be converted into their silver salts and their composition analyzed by combustion; hydroxy esters also can be investigated by benzoylation. The orthodox determination of acetyl values usually applied to ascertain the number of alcoholic hydroxyl groups as, for instance, in oils, does not yield conclusive figures for natural copals.

Another way of introducing alcoholic hydroxyl groups into copal-type synthetics is connected with the principles of producing phenol modified ethers and esters, as described in the author's U. S. Patents Nos. 2,268,946 and 2,268,947, and described in detail in a previous chapter.

The free alcoholic hydroxyl groups characteristic of copal-type synthetics are highly reactive with fatty acids. They do not enter into reaction, however, with high molecular resinous acids or resinous anhydrides. They, therefore, do not interfere with the acidic material which, to a small extent, is always present with them in the same resin. They also do not interact with each other by the linking up of two hydroxyls of two different molecules with the elimination of water, a reaction which would be equivalent to an inner ether formation. Ethers are very stable compounds which are not subject to saponification, and their formation would reduce saponification numbers. Actually, saponification values do not decrease during the production of copal-type synthetics, and also not on their further heating, giving evidence that no ether formation takes place.

In order to assist in

the depolymerization process,

which is one of the essential phases in the production of copal-type synthetics, the presence of a substantial amount of permanently fusible resins, particularly highly polymerized rosin esters, is desirable. Primarily they act as fluxing materials which facilitate the fusion and prevent local decomposition and charring during the gelling and degelling cycle. They may also, at the same time, enter the process chemically, forming mixed esters by interchange reactions with the substances whose depolymerization they have assisted as fluxing materials.

A further aid in the degradation of reversible resin gels are peptizing agents, as they are well known in colloid chemistry. Peptizers are required only in small amounts, and it is not necessary to make additions of them in the case of copal-type synthetic resins, because they are present in the batch in the form of acid decomposition products, originating within the mass during the polymerizing and degelling process. Such peptizing agents have the ability to penetrate into the gelled particles, breaking them up into smaller units, and to disperse them within the liquid portion of the surrounding medium.

To explain the peptizing action, reference is made to a well known procedure in the running of copal gums. If straight Congo gum is melted alone, without any additions, until a weight loss of 25% is reached, only limited solubility is obtained. Using diphenylamine as a yardstick for solubility, it is found that the Congo, fused to this amount of loss, is insoluble in diphenylamine. If, on the other hand, the same Congo gum is run in the same way, to the same weight loss, but melted with a small addition of 5-10% rosin, the final product is completely soluble in diphenylamine. In actually carrying out this fusion, it can be clearly seen that the whole melting procedure is changed in character. The tough and stringy foam of the rosin-free batch is changed into a loose, easily breakable type of foam by the presence of rosin. Orthodox fluxing materials can create this surprising effect only if added in considerable quantities; and it is, therefore, obvious that the small rosin addition in this case acts as a true peptizer.

The manufacture of copal-type synthetics, as has been previously explained, is the process of building up large molecular aggregates and, subsequently, breaking them down again into smaller units. This requires special

equipment and machinery.

The heating equipment must be able to generate large amounts of heat at high temperature ranges within short periods of time. An efficient cooling system must be available in order to bring the kettle temperature down quickly below the region of gelation. The time and temperature period of gelation is dangerous because reversible gels might convert into irreversible gels, if held too long at gelation temperature; as a result, agitation stops and a fire may start. The stirring equipment requires a powerful motor to keep the agitator moving while the heated resin is in the process of gelatinization. Thorough mechanical mixing is of the greatest importance at this stage of the process, in order to equalize the temperature within the kettle, to avoid decomposition, partial overpolymerization, and possible charring or even burning. Strong foam breakers are necessary to handle the heavy foaming which accompanies the processing. The maximum temperature to be reached depends upon the temperature at which the particular resinous ester gelatinizes, and has to be 20-40° C. higher than the gelation temperature. As a rule the peak temperature varies between 270° and 325° C.

In the early stages of the process of depolymerization, pressure is applied, to keep acid decomposition products, which act as peptizing and dispersing agents, within the kettle. As soon as dispersion is sufficiently advanced, as evidenced by a decreasing viscosity of the kettle content, the pressure is released. Finally, prolonged and steady vacuum is applied until practically all volatile matter is eliminated.

When the finished copal-type synthetics are unloaded from the kettle, a decided copal-like odor, known from Congo copal running, is often noticed. It is obviously an odor produced by the degradation of highly polymerized material. As in copal running, the depolymerization process in the manufacture of copal-type synthetics is accompanied by a considerable loss of weight.

To explain further the interesting principles in the production of copal-like synthetic resins,

two typical cases

are cited, recording the changes in their characteristics during the procedure.

Table 11. Changes of Resin Constants During Gelling and Degelling

	Temperature of Batch				
	240° C.	*260° C.*	*280° C.*	*310° C.*	*280° C.*
Time of processing	10 hours	18 hours	25 hours	30 hours	34 hours
Acid value	30	28	26	19	18
Melting point	142° C.	145° C.	155° C.	150° C.	145° C.
Viscosity	O	U	Z	X	U
Solubility expressed by titration	20 c.c.	15 c.c.	12 c.c.	18 c.c.	24 c.c.
Solubility expressed by clearing temperature	260° C.	270° C.	290° C.	240° C.	190° C.
Condition of batch	Liquid	Liquid	Incipient gelation	Slightly gelatinous	Liquid

The first case is described in *Table 11*, giving the changes in constants during gelling and degelling. The tabulation registers acid values, melting points, viscosities, and solubilities of samples taken from a production batch after different times of processing, and at various batch temperatures. The viscosity is expressed by the Gardner scale as that of a 60% resin solution in xylol. The solubility is given as number of c.c. in titrating to cloud point 10 grams of a 60% resin solution in xylol with mineral spirits. It is also given as the temperature at which a clear solution is obtained, when the resin is heated up with two parts of Z body linseed oil. It can be seen that the peak of the gelatinization process in this particular case is reached after between 25 and 30 hours of treatment, and at a point when the viscosity is at its highest and the solubility at its lowest level.

The tabulation serves well to define the character of the copal-like esters, particularly by comparing the sample taken after 18 hours of treatment with that taken after 33 hours. Both samples are taken from a liquid, non-gelatinous batch, have the same melting point and viscosity, and outwardly look exactly alike. However, due to the fact that the material of the second sample has passed through the process of gelling and degelling, it has acquired entirely different properties.

Its solubility is greatly improved both in volatile solvents and oil. Expressed in c.c. of mineral spirits titration, its solubility has increased 60% in volatile solvents. In drying oil it has improved to the extent that the point of clarification in bodied linseed oil drops from 270° to 190° C. Normally, solubility improves while melting points and viscosities decrease within the same resin group. It is true in this case, however, to a much smaller degree than in other resin groups. The gelling and degelling procedure, therefore, makes it possible to vastly increase solubility without substantially decreasing melting point or viscosity.

The internal structure of the second sample is basically different from that of the first sample. The resin before degradation does not give complete solutions even in strong solvents, but segregates insoluble or swelling particles, which can be separated from the bulk of the solution by filtration. After the resin has passed through the degelling process, it dissolves completely even in weak solvents, indicating the vanishing of overpolymerized parts. The fact that, in spite of this, the viscosity of the two samples is alike, proves that low-molecular portions also disappear, leading to a higher degree of molecular homogeneity.

The gelling and degelling process

also produces resins of higher bodying speeds, as can be proved by comparing the two resin samples in question. For this purpose, one part of the resin is heated up with two parts of Z_2 bodied linseed oil to 300° C., and held there until a viscosity of G is reached, when a sample is thinned with an equal amount of mineral spirits. The time necessary to attain this viscosity is usually called the bodying time; it amounts to 100 minutes for the first sample and to only 70 minutes for the second sample. The increased bodying speed is mainly due to the fact that no time is lost for degelling in the second case, whereas the gelled material of the first sample requires considerable time for the destruction of the false body due to its overpolymerized parts.

When the two samples taken after 18 and 33 hours respectively, are compared for heat stability, a substantial difference appears which is of great economic importance, as heat losses increase the material costs of surface coatings and printing inks. The determination is carried out by heating 300 grams of the samples to 285° C., in a 600 c. c. beaker, holding it at this temperature for two hours, and then determining the loss in weight. The first sample loses 4%, the second sample only ½% in weight, proving an eightfold increase in heat stability.

Another typical case of producing copal-like resinous esters is demonstrated through the graph of *Figure 8* showing the change of viscosity and molecular weight during the time of processing. The change in viscosity during the interesting phase of gelation, is pictured in two different ways, first in terms of the Gardner scale for a solution of 60 parts of resin in 40 parts of xylol, and secondly in terms of amperes, showing

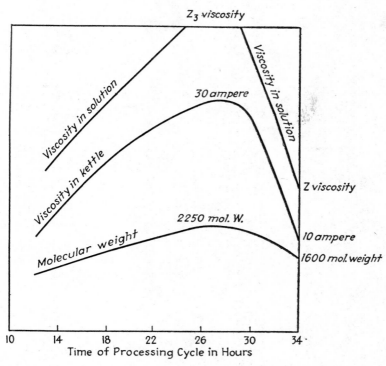

FIGURE 8. Changes of viscosity and molecular weight in the process of gelling and degelling.

the relative electric energy necessary to turn the agitator of the resin kettle.

The change of viscosity of the resin, measured in solution, surpasses the scale of the graph during the peak of the gelling and degelling period. The whole range of the viscosity change, however, is clearly shown by the change in the resistance which the resin offers to agitation while processed in the kettle, expressed in terms of electric energy. It reaches a high point at about 28 hours, declining rapidly thereafter.

The molecular size of the copal-type synthetic increases during the gelling period, reaching a maximum of about 2250 when the resin viscosity is at its highest point, and decreases slowly during the degelling period, reaching a

molecular weight of 1700 to 1900

when the batch is completely liquified. The first signs of gelatinization appear when the molecular size exceeds the value of 2000 on the upward cycle, and gelatinous particles begin to vanish distinctly on the downward trend, when the molecular weight declines below 2000. This phenomenon is a confirmation of the general rule that the molecular weight of completely soluble and non-gelatinous resins of the class under consideration is restricted to an upper limit of 2000.

Comparing the molecular conditions of copal-type synthetics, made by means of depolymerization of gelatinous material, to that of resins made by means of molecular agglomeration in the maturing process, it appears that the molecular weights in both cases are very nearly the same, the only difference being that copal-type synthetics reached their molecular size from the upper level and the matured resins from the lower level.

There exists a striking analogy between the origin of copal gums, fossilized by nature, followed by their treatment in the varnish kettle, to the production of copal-type synthetics which are polymerized first, and later degraded. This similarity accounts for the fact that the properties of copal-type synthetics approach closely many of the characteristics of fused copals.

Copal-type synthetics have outstanding solubility in both oils and other synthetic resins and possess great heat stability, with the result that during the treatment in the varnish kettle they suffer a heat loss which is only a fraction of the loss undergone by other synthetic resins, such as orthodox maleics or phenolics.

They have genuine viscosity which is not decreased by the heat of varnish cooking, quite in contrast to the false body found in many high viscosity resins made by polymerization only. Resins with false body are physical mixtures of several resin portions of various degrees of viscosity, ranging from relatively low to very high degrees of polymerization. The actually measured viscosity of such resins is the arithmetical mean of the low viscosity portions and the portions of high viscosity. A part of the latter may be overpolymerized even to a highly gelatinous condition.

On further heating of such a resin, either alone or with oil, its gelatinous portion is degelled and liquified to a more or less fluid state. Thereby the total or average viscosity of the resin, determined by the usual method, is decreased, offering the typical performance of resins with false body. Copal-type synthetics never show this peculiar phenomenon because, due to their mode of preparation, they are in a state of uniform molecular size and do not contain any overpolymerized parts, which are liable to degel.

Due to their method of manufacturing, copal-type synthetics possess a high degree of

resistance to chemical agents;

however, in spite of this capacity, copal-type synthetics possess good chemical reactivity with fatty acids and oils, especially linseed oil, a property which is of great practical importance to the varnish maker. The reactivity of the resins is based on the two factors—acidity and hydroxyl content. The resinous acids or anhydride present are those that are not drawn off when vacuum is applied at high temperature and, therefore, are of a highly non-volatile nature. Due to this peculiarity, they are able to set free and expel volatile fatty acids, originating in the heat decomposition of the oil, and thereby are capable of chemically linking resin and oil together. As explained elsewhere, resinous acids or anhydrides have the ability to drive off fatty acids at the heat of varnish cooking.

The other base for chemical reactions between resins and oils are the free alcoholic hydroxyl groups, which are present in copal-type synthetics in amounts of several per cent, as indicated by acetyl values. These hydroxyl groups are able to esterify with fatty acids as such, or fatty carboxyl groups of partially split oils, both of which are present in drying varnish oils either initially or are formed during the varnish-cooking process. In order to demonstrate this type of resin-oil reaction, a light colored copal-type synthetic, with an acid value of 5, is heated for two hours at 265° C. with the same amount of a linseed oil-fatty acid of an acidity of 185. If no reaction took place, the melt would yield an acid value of 95, whereas the actual determination shows an acid value of only 50, thereby giving evidence that a vivid reaction has occurred between resin and fatty acids.

As a consequence of

resin-oil reactivity

copal-type synthetics show quick bodying and speedy drying with oils, especially with linseed oil. For the same reason the varnish films are of outstanding mechanical toughness and rigidity, quite comparable to those of fossil gum varnishes.

Copal-type synthetics possess the properties of both natural gums and synthetic resins, balanced in a way to suit most practical purposes. If, for special purposes, a copal-type synthetic is required to approach in its characteristics very closely the properties of natural gums, fossil copals like Congo, Manila or Kauri copals may be incorporated as such into the synthetics, after they have been solubilized by proper methods. The following experiment serves to demonstrate the effect of natural gums in such combinations. 20 parts of a solubilized fossil gum were incorporated into 100 parts of rosin, and melting point and molecular weight of the resulting product were determined. The values obtained for the total combination could easily be calculated for the straight copal portion, and the figures thus found for the copal alone appeared to be of a high order of magnitude, *i.e.* 220° C. for the melting point and 1250 for the molecular weight. The values apply to the non-esterified material; according to practical experience, esterification will increase both the melting point and the molecular weight.

The simplest method of incorporating natural gums into copal-type synthetics consists in

running the copal

separately in the orthodox way, and then fusing it with the other component. This method, however, does not bring out the merits of the copal, because the prolonged heating at the extremely high temperature of more than 325° C., which is required in the running process, breaks down the molecular structure to such an extent that serious damage is done to the chemical and physical characteristics of the copal.

This damage appears clearly from the decrease in molecular weight of copals during the running process. The molecular weight of the raw Congo copal, for instance, is so high, that it cannot be determined in the usual way because the material is not completely soluble in diphenylamine. Even if a Congo copal is depolymerized to the extent of 10% loss, *i.e.* if it is subjected to a so-called slack melt, it still remains imperfectly soluble and its molecular weight is far beyond the 2000 line. It is only when the heating losses exceed 20% and depolymerization is assisted by a peptizing agent like rosin, that molecular weights drop under 2000 and become determinable. At 25% loss, a molecular weight of 1200 is reached and at 50% loss it is found to be less than 600, approaching the molecular weight of ordinary rosin.

The last named figure shows clearly the destructive action of orthodox copal running. The nature of the chemical changes occurring during the process can only be guessed from the drop in acid value and the amount of decomposition products. These substances consist of non-volatile hydrocarbon-like copal oils of high boiling point and, furthermore, consist of volatile products, such as carbon dioxide and water. Also, to a small extent, formic and acetic acid are formed and escape. The result of such changes is a greatly reduced chemical reactivity of run copals with oils, and a decided deterioration of physical properties manifested by a decrease of toughness, the development of a rosin-like brittleness and a considerable darkening of the color.

A more suitable method of introducing natural gums into copal-type synthetics consists in solubilizing copal gums without the obvious drawbacks cited before. The method is based on the

mastication of copals

as described in the Author's U.S. Patents Nos. 2,007,333; 2,101,398; 2,110,803. This procedure does not apply heat to make copals soluble and compatible with synthetic resins, but uses mechanical force to achieve this purpose. The gums are kneaded in a heavy mixer type machine like a Banbury mixer, at a temperature at which the copal becomes sufficiently plastic, to allow the kneading blades to rotate, and to prevent grinding and pulverizing effects. The copal is fed slowly but continuously into one end of the machine by pressure pistons, which can exert pressures of several hundred pounds per square inch. While the mixer is operating, the gum is extruded at the other end of the device through a small opening. The outcoming thread of masticated copal is conveyed to a heavily built rubber calender with closely spaced rollers. The calender rolls the copal into thin sheets, which are taken off the machine when they are thoroughly homogenized. After cooling, the sheets of masticated material are broken up into small pieces and are now ready for incorporation into copal-type synthetics.

The factors of time, temperature and pressure in the mastication process vary within practical limits, learned by experience, and are adapted to the particular types of copals used and to the special effects wanted in connection with resin manufacture.

There is a further possibility of varying the mastication process by applying vacuum in the second step of the procedure, while the material is being treated on the calender rollers. This is done by using a device, similar to a totally enclosed roller mill, which is equipped with heating units. The vacuum accelerates the removal of volatile products and facilitates certain phases of the procedure.

Masticated gums offer many advantages over fused copals. They suffer an appreciably lower processing loss, keep their original color better and retain much more of their valuable initial properties of physical rigidity and chemical resistance. While they do not become as completely soluble in other resins as fused copals, they reach, nevertheless, a

degree of solubility

which makes them readily fusible and easily compatible with synthetic resins.

The effect of mastication on the solubility of Congo copal is demonstrated quantitatively by the following experiment. Ten parts each of raw Congo, masticated Congo, and Congo, fused to the extent of 10% weight loss, *i.e.* so-called slack melt Congo, were heated to 100° C. with 100 parts of diphenylamine. All three samples were then allowed to cool under identical conditions and the freezing point depression of the diphenylamine was determined. All three copals were only partially soluble in diphenylamine and the depression, therefore, was a measure of the degree of solubility, because the depression increased, the more material was going into solution. The following depressions were found: 0.20° C. for raw Congo, 0.40° C. for slack melt Congo and 1.00° C. for masticated Congo, proving that the masticated copal was five times more soluble than raw Congo and $2\frac{1}{2}$ times more soluble than the copal that had been depolymerized by heat to a loss of 10%.

The mastication process also serves to make copals, especially Congo copal, soluble in ethyl alcohol and it has been found that the best solubilizing effect for this purpose is obtained by kneading the gums at low temperature, occasionally using pressure at the same time. The fact that the entirely spirit-insoluble Congo copal can be rendered fully soluble in ethyl alcohol is an achievement that may gain great technical importance, because it makes a new material, which is available in large quantities, usable for the production of spirit varnishes.

Mastication furthermore decreases the

viscosity of copals

when dissolved in other resins, oils or solvents. This effect is of importance for the incorporation of natural copals into synthetic resins, especially copal-type synthetics. The lowering of the viscosity can be demonstrated by the example of soft Manila copals, which find wide industrial use as shellac substitutes. While Manila copals are more or less alcohol-soluble by themselves, their solutions, in ethyl alcohol are highly viscous and often have a stringy character which makes their use impracticable. After mastication, Manila copals yield non-viscous, non-stringy and easily workable spirit varnishes. For instance, a spirit-soluble Manila copal, which gave a 50% alcohol solution of the viscosity S on the Gardner scale yielded, after mastication, a 50% solution of as low a viscosity as D.

As appears from the foregoing chapter, many of the conceptions of copal-type synthetics have their origin in

the old antagonism

between the two groups of natural and synthetic resins. However, the detailed study of the principles underlying their structure, their production and their properties, proves that copal-type synthetics are a new resin class which closes the gap between the two opponents, combining the good properties of both groups. Being a more recent development, this field is wide open for further research work. Already today, a number of valuable varieties are available, based on the various types of the resins used as the starting material for the new method of processing, *i.e.* the phenolic, the maleic or the natural copal varieties with many other possibilities of variation by means of different combinations of these types.

Chapter V

Chemical Characteristics of Resins

The detailed comments on the composition and production of coating and ink resins make it clear that a great variety of resins exists in every one of the four resin groups under discussion, *i.e.* the pure phenol resins, the modified phenolics, the maleic resins and the copal-type synthetics. The comments also make it clear that there is a definite need for reliable methods for their characterization.

The many resin types are

identified and evaluated by well defined characteristics

which cover the properties of both the resins themselves and those of their combinations with drying oils. The characteristics involved are manifold; they concern chemical properties, the melting point and viscosity, the relationship between resins and solvents as well as between resins and oils. They furthermore concern drying and gloss problems, and questions of film resistance. Each of the property characteristics is particularly pronounced in specific resin types, and has its own noteworthy importance in each of the two classes of surface coating and printing ink resins.

This chapter deals with the chemical characteristics of the resins, *i.e.* their acidity, behavior on saponification, hydroxyl content and oil reactivity, oxidation and heat resistance; and furthermore, deals with questions of chemical analysis and molecular weight. Two subsequent chapters discuss the specific influence of physical resin characteristics and of the properties of resin-oil combinations on the performance of surface coatings and printing inks.

150

Discussing the chemical resin characteristics, it appears that only a few are accessible to accurate analytical determinations, *i.e.* the acidity, the characteristics of saponification, the amount of unsaponifiable matter, and the molecular weight. In addition, it is possible to determine, with some degree of accuracy, the acetyl value, the iodine number, the degree of heat stability and the oxygen-absorption figure, but only in exceptional cases is it feasible to determine, qualitatively, the chemical constituents of the resins; and in no case is it possible to carry out quantitative analyses.

Due to the presence of neutralizable groups, all coating and ink resins

possess a certain acidity

which, as a rule, varies between the acid values of 15 and 35. Very neutral copal-type synthetics have acid values as low as 3-5, non-esterified modified phenolics as high as 100-130, and partially or entirely non-esterified maleic or fumaric resins as high as 150-315. Pure phenol resins show apparent acid numbers between 40 and 100, which do not indicate acidity, but are caused by a reaction of the alkali, used for titration, with the free phenolic hydroxyl groups present.

To express acidity in terms of weight, the molecular size of the acidic material has to be taken into account. Assuming the molecular weight to be about 600, acid values would roughly indicate the amount of acid substances in percentage of weight. Accordingly, normal resins contain an amount of acidic material, which is too high to be considered merely as an impurity.

An amount of about 15 to 25% of

free acidity is desirable

in many coating and ink resins. It allows better control of the bodying with oils, speeds up drying, improves adhesion, prevents floating in tinted enamels and, particularly, it promotes

the formation of needle-shaped soap crystals during the ageing process of lead and zinc containing paint films, which
thereby are reinforced in a mechanical and chemical way.
This process can be made visible under the polarizing microscope, as is shown in *Figure 9*. In the left hand photograph
the long elastic lead soap needles are visible, while in the
right hand photograph the short brittle zinc soap crystals can
be seen.

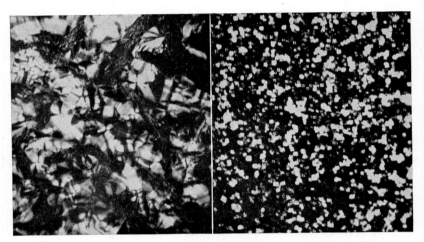

FIGURE 9.   Soap crystal formation in lead and zinc paints.

Acidic substances in resins of normal acidity, not exceeding
acid values of 35, have little detrimental effect on resin performance in actual practice, because they are diluted to low
concentrations and are present mainly as anhydrides, or mixed
acid-anhydrides, which show only weak, or practically no, acid
reaction in coating and ink materials, and develop a distinct
acidic character only in the presence of water.

Acid values in resins higher than 40 are, as a rule, undesirable in most cases; they are liable to cause livering with basic
pigments in paints and enamels, and they reduce the weather
resistance of surface coatings because resinous acids and
anhydrides are weak spots, open to attacks by oxygen and
water.

The method of determination of acid values has been the object of many controversies. A reliable procedure is the following:

The resin is dissolved in a mixture of 65 parts of nitration xylol and 35 parts of denatured alcohol, containing 5% water. This mixture is neutralized by adding a few drops of 10N alcoholic potassium hydroxide until a light pink color is obtained, using phenolphthalein as indicator. Then one gram of the powdered resin, weighed out accurately and placed into a 250 c.c. Erlenmeyer flask, is dissolved in 100 c.c. of the above mixture. When the solution is complete, 5 drops of the standard phenolphthalein solution is added, and the titration is carried out with 10N alcoholic potassium hydroxide. The number of c.c. used, multiplied by 5.6 gives the acid number directly.

Modified maleics give an indistinct end point, with the red color fading away in a few minutes. For practical purposes, the titration at which the color persists for 20-30 seconds may be considered the final point.

Using 95% alcohol in the acid value determination, sufficient water is present in the beginning and during the titration to convert

resinous anhydrides or mixed acid anhydrides

into acids. If the titration is carried out in the absence of water by using carefully dehydrated solvents, practically no acidity is found. For instance, an ester gum that has an acid value of 12 according to the orthodox method of determination, will yield only a value of 0.5, when the determination is carried out with waterfree ingredients.

To determine the acidity of dark colored resins, the use of an aqueous sodium chloride solution has been recommended, to make visible the color change of the indicator. As a rule, however, it is preferable to use instead very low resin concentrations in order to make the color of the solution lighter, because aqueous liquids create two-phase systems which may cause other errors. It has been found, for instance, that if maleics are titrated with a water layer, acid numbers are obtained which are far below the true values.

Subjecting the resins under consideration in this technological study to saponification, it is found that all rosin based

ester resins are saponifiable.

Pure phenolics yield figures identical with the alkali titration of the acid value determination, *i.e.* values which are due to the reactivity of free phenolic hydroxyl groups.

Among the rosin-based esters the modified phenol resins have the lowest saponification values, varying from 180-190, maleic resins the highest numbers, between 230 and 240, with copal-type synthetics occupying a middle position of 200-210. Due to these typical differences, saponification values are a help in the identification of resin groups.

All of the above resins offer great resistance to saponification. Whereas vegetable oils are quickly and completely saponified by refluxing with alcoholic potassium hydroxide, this procedure cannot be used to carry to completion the saponification of the resins under discussion, even if a large excess of potassium hydroxide is used and the boiling under reflux is continued for hours. To obtain complete saponification it is necessary to use solvents with boiling points higher than that of ethyl alcohol. Pyridine has been suggested for this purpose, but the most suitable solvent is butanol in combination with toluol, employed in the following manner:

10 grams of resin are dissolved in 50 c.c. of toluol and the solution diluted with toluol to yield exactly 100 c.c. To this solution is added 50 c.c. of 1N potassium hydroxide in butanol, and the mixture is heated to boiling under a reflux condenser. Samples of 15 c.c. each are withdrawn every hour for back-titration until constant values are obtained. In spite of the fact that, under the specified conditions, even heavy-bodied

oils are saponified instantaneously, several hours are required to complete the saponification of the resins.

The same procedure also furnishes a good idea of the speed with which various resin types are saponified. The differences in

speed of saponification

of typical resins are recorded in the graph of *Figure 10,* picturing the relationship between the time of saponification in hours and the portion of saponified material in percentage of the total of saponifiable matter present.

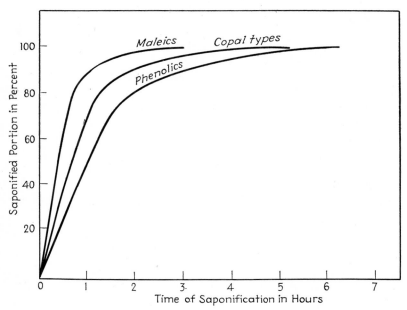

FIGURE 10. Speed of saponification of resins.

The three curves make it clear that the maleics saponify fastest, with 95% saponified after one hour, followed in speed by the copal-type synthetics, with 75% saponified after one hour, and finally the modified phenolics, which are the slowest in saponification speed, with only 60% saponified after one hour.

The neutralization of acidic matter and the saponification of ester-like substances by means of alkali helps in obtaining a closer insight into resin composition, because it makes possible the separation of acidic, saponifiable, unsaponifiable and alcoholic substances, to be followed by the further investigation of the isolated portions.

Separation and isolation

can be carried out according to the following general procedure. A more elaborate method is described in detail in the chapter dealing with "Reactivities between Resins and Oils."

In order to isolate the acidic material present, either as free resinous acids or anhydrides, the resin is dissolved in toluol, and titrated to neutrality with $10N$ aqueous potassium hydroxide. After adding water, the toluol resin solution is separated from the aqueous soap solution. The latter is acidified with diluted hydrochloric acid, whereby the free resinous acids are precipitated. They are then easily isolated by the usual methods.

For the purpose of isolating the unsaponifiable material present in the resin, the resin-toluol solution, separated from the aqueous layer, is boiled under reflux with an excess of $1N$ potassium hydroxide solution in butanol for three hours, after which all resinous esters are saponified. The reaction liquid is then evaporated to dryness on the water bath, using additions of ethyl alcohol to drive off the toluol. The dry residue is finally taken up with a large amount of water and the soap solution so obtained is extracted several times with benzol. Small additions of alcohol are helpful in breaking up emulsions. The combined benzol extracts contain the unsaponifiable matter of the resin, isolated as such by evaporation of the solvents.

If material appears, which is neither soluble in the water layer nor in the benzol portion, it is indicative of the presence of higher molecular alcohols, such as polypentaerythritols, in the resin.

In order to isolate the resinous acids, which are present in the form of saponifiable esters, the aqueous portion of the previous analytical step is acidified by diluted hydrochloric acid, whereby the acidic material is precipitated. It is separated by solvent from the acid water solution and is then isolated quantitatively.

The remaining aqueous portion contains hydrochloric acid, water soluble salts, organic acids, and most of the esterifying alcohols used in producing the resin.

A very important characteristic of synthetic resins is their

molecular weight.

As pointed out in a previous chapter, it can be determined very accurately by the classic method of freezing point depression, according to Beckmann, using comparatively large amounts of solvent and proper equipment to exclude any disturbing outside influences.

The apparatus used for the determination of molecular weights is pictured in *Figure 11*. It consists of a metal stand with the necessary clamps, a variable speed motor with coupling, flexible shaft and propeller with steady bearing, located in the rubber stopper on top of the 500 c.c. wide mouth reaction flask. The latter is immersed in an oil bath which is heated electrically. In the same stopper is placed the Beckmann differential thermometer, which covers a range of 6° C. and is calibrated to one one-hundredth of a degree.

To carry out the determination, 450 grams of purified diphenylamine are placed in the flask and 45 grams of powdered resin added. The resin is dissolved by previously and separately heating the mixture to about 80° C. The flask is then put into the oil bath at room temperature, which first acts as a cooling agent for the inserted flask and later as a medium to maintain the temperature of the diphenylamine

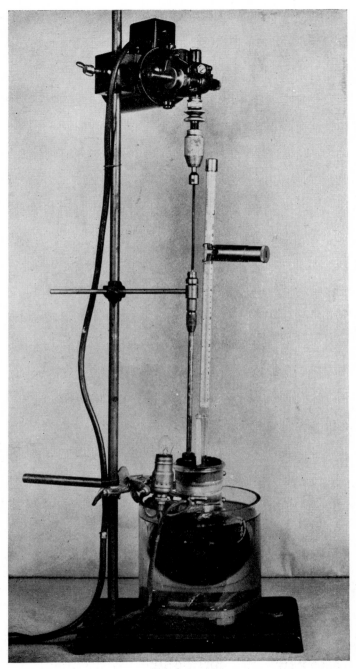

FIGURE 11. Apparatus for the determination of the molecular weight of resins.

within a few degrees of its freezing point. The connection with the motor is then made, the mixture allowed to cool down to within 1-2° C. of the predetermined freezing point, and the Beckmann thermometer is inserted after its column of mercury is properly adjusted.

On cooling, the temperature on the thermometer drops 2-3° C. below the actual freezing point and then rapidly recovers to reach the true freezing point temperature, stopping suddenly within one one-hundredth of a degree and remaining constant for several minutes. In order to check this point, the diphenylamine resin mixture may be remelted by gentle heating of the oil bath, and the cooling procedure repeated.

The determination of molecular weights is an operation which consumes too much time to be usable for routine resin testing, but it is a good tool for scientific and technical development work. It has also a place in analytical practice. because it is an aid to the

identification of resin classes.

As a guide for this purpose, the following molecular weights are cited:

Ester Resins

Rosin-glycerine ester	775– 825
Rosin-pentaerythritol ester	950–1000

Pure Phenol Resins

Acid-condensed amyl phenol resin M.P. 90° C.	650– 700
Acid-condensed butyl phenol resin M.P. 135° C	850– 900
Alkali-condensed butyl phenol resin M.P. 90° C.	750– 800

Modified Phenolics

Rosin-modified phenol resin M.P. 140° C.	1200–1300
Rosin-modified phenol resin M.P. 160° C.	1300–1400
Rosin-modified phenolic, non-esterified	1100–1200

Modified Maleics

Rosin-modified maleic resin M.P. 130°–150° C.	1200–1400
Rosin-modified maleic, non-esterified	625– 675
Rosin-modified maleic, partially gelled	2000–2100

Copal-type Synthetics

Copal-type synthetic resin M.P. 140°–150° C.	1700–1900

Another important characteristic of resins is their

ability to react with drying oils

a capability which is based essentially on the presence of phenolic hydroxyl groups, alcoholic hydroxyls and non-volatile acidic substances in the resins, as explained in the chapter on "Chemical Fundamentals of Coating and Ink Resins."

Free phenolic hydroxyl groups in pure phenol resins can be determined quantitatively by alkali titration. This cannot be done accurately in the case of modified phenolics, because alkali titration values also reflect free resin acidity, which cannot be determined separately from phenolic hydroxyls.

Free alcoholic hydroxyl groups in pure phenol resins can be determined quantitatively by taking the total acetyl value and subtracting the alkali titration value. Their number cannot be measured accurately in this way in rosin-based ester resins, such as modified phenolics, maleics or copal-type synthetics, because acetic anhydride reacts not only with alcoholic groups but also with certain non-alcoholic ones present in the rosin component. Due to such additional reactivities, acetyl values do not furnish accurate figures for the number of free alcoholic hydroxyl groups. They permit, however, comparisons to be made between various resin classes. For instance, the

acetyl values

of copal-type synthetics, being of the exceptionally high order of 150, compared to less than 100 for other resin groups, indicate relatively large percentages of alcoholic groups in this resin class.

Another method of obtaining an approximate estimate of free hydroxyls present, consists in heating the resins with free linseed oil fatty acid for two hours at 270° C. and determining the drop in acid value. The larger the decrease, the higher the percentage of alcoholic hydroxyls.

Oil reactivity of resinous esters also depends on the presence of

heat stable non-volatile acidic material

which expels volatile fatty acids from the oil, thereby linking resin and oil together. The degree of heat stability of a resin, therefore, is a good measure of its oil reactivity.

A good method of determining heat stability is the following: 300 grams of resin, weighed in a 600 c.c. beaker, are heated in one hour to 285° C. and held at this temperature for one hour, after which time the heat loss is determined. In case of foaming, some stirring is necessary.

Tested in this way, high class coating and ink resins show relatively small heat losses, *i.e.* maleics suffer 2%, modified phenolics 1.5%, copal-type synthetics very low losses of 1% or less. Resins of low heat resistance may show losses of up to 10%.

Pure phenol resins cannot be evaluated from the standpoint of heat stability, because the acid-condensed, and especially the alkali-catalyzed resins, are not finished resinous products, but must be considered as active chemicals which enter into chemical reactions with the oils, causing considerable heat losses, due to the elimination of volatile reaction products.

Heat stability of resins is a very important economic factor, distinctly influencing the

cost of varnish making.

During the process of resin dissolution in the oil and the procedure of varnish cooking which follows, the resins are exposed to the destructive influence of considerable heat for long periods of time. To withstand this action, the resins must have a high degree of heat stability. If they do not possess the necessary heat resistance, they suffer substantial material losses while being incorporated into the oils, to such an extent that their use often proves uneconomical. Very often resins made in open varnish kettles, without the use of vacuum, undergo such losses.

An important chemical characteristic of resins from the practical standpoint is their

tendency to oxidize.

The tendency to oxidation is comparatively small or, expressed conversely, the resistance to oxidation is relatively great in high class resins. Its degree can be judged from the discoloration of the resins in thin layers, from their oxygen-absorption values and from their iodine numbers.

If thin layers of resins as such, or in combination with small amounts of other substances, such as oils, plasticizers or nitrocellulose, are exposed to the action of light and air, the resins begin to darken, the discoloration indicating the start of the oxidation process which continues to progress during the life of the resin film.

The color of most of the resins under consideration is of light grade, varying between WG and K, when graded by the standards of the official color scale of the U.S. Department of Agriculture, which is shown in *Figure 12*. This interesting

photograph of the rosin color standards

was taken with transmitted light, the test cubes being placed on a ground glass plate, with strong diffused illumination from below. The exposure time had to be adjusted within fractions of a second, in order to obtain the true and correct color values as shown in the illustration.

FIGURE 12.   Official rosin color standards.

In determining the color grade of resins by comparing the cubes, it must be borne in mind that such a comparison, if a remelting of the resin is required, is not reliable because considerable darkening may take place on fusion. In such cases, color comparison in solutions is preferred, using one of the standard colorimeters. Sometimes allowance must be made for a certain discrepancy in the shade of coloring.

The degree of discoloration of the various resins under consideration, when exposed to oxidizing influences in thin layers, varies greatly. Maleic resins possess the best light stability, followed closely by copal-type synthetics. Modified phenolics show pronounced discoloration, increasing with the amount of phenolic component present. Pure phenolics show the strongest tendencies to darken.

It has been suggested that the resistance of resins to oxidation be measured by means of

the oxygen bomb test

used in organic chemistry. For this purpose 10 grams of the resin, pulverized and screened to a standardized particle size, are exposed in the bomb to pure oxygen at room temperature under a pressure of 300 pounds per square inch for one week, and after this period the increase in resin weight is determined. The oxygen-absorption values are about 3% for ester gum, 2% for maleics, 1% for modified phenolics and less than 1/2 of 1% for copal-type synthetics.

Due to the fact that the ability of resins to absorb halogen is proportional to their tendency to absorb oxygen, the oxidation-resistance of resins can also be judged from the amount of free iodine which they are able to absorb, as is indicated by

the traditional iodine value.

Iodine values vary with the methods used for their determination. Reproducible figures were obtained for this technological study by using the Wiys solution. Iodine numbers of phenolic and maleic coating and ink resins obtained by the Wiys method are, as a rule, in the order of 100. They are considerably higher for copal-type synthetics and are reduced pronouncedly in phenolics and maleics, when these resins are subjected to the maturing procedure.

The chemical characteristics of resins are necessarily closely related to

their chemical composition

and for many reasons and purposes it is desirable to determine qualitatively and quantitatively the resin constituents. The possibilities for accurate analyses are limited because, in most cases during the resin-making process, the components undergo radical chemical changes or completely lose their identity.

Among the quantitative determinations, the ash content of resins can be easily analyzed in the usual way by the burning of a weighed amount of the resin and calcining the residue to constant weight. Ash contents are negligibly small in all coating and ink resins discussed in this book.

Another quantitative analysis which can be carried out with some degree of accuracy, is the determination of the amount of

the esterifying alcohols

used in resin manufacture. For this purpose the resin sample is saponified completely according to methods previously described, using potassium hydroxide, dissolved in butanol. The soap solution is evaporated to dryness and the residue is taken up with water. The aqueous solution is then acidified with an excess of hydrochloric acid and again evaporated to dryness on the water bath. This step is particularly necessary in the case of the pentaerythritol resins being analyzed, in order to destroy the toluol-soluble formals, which are always formed during resin production by the interaction of the pentaerythritol with small amounts of formaldehyde, originating from the heat decomposition of the pentaerythritol.

The residue, remaining after evaporation, is suspended or dissolved, in at least ten times its weight of water, and the suspension or solution is extracted several times with toluol. The water layer, finally separated from the toluol, contains those portions of the esterifying alcohols used in resin production, which have not lost their identity in the manufacturing procedure.

Glycols can be isolated by the evaporation of the aqueous solution to dryness on the water bath, and extraction with absolute alcohol. The glycerine content of the aqueous solution can be determined quantitatively by the normal analytical procedure of the bichromate or acetine methods, after the water-soluble organic acids have been removed by precipitation as lead compounds. The pentaerythritol content is determined by precipitation with benzaldehyde according to methods described in the literature.

Polypentaerythritols offer difficulties in their quantitative analysis. During the resin-making process, a substantial portion of the polypentaerythritols enter into complex reactions among themselves and with other components present, with the result that unsaponifiable substances are formed, which are partially soluble in toluol and, therefore, do not enter the aqueous phase during the course of the analysis.

All other resin tests are only

of a qualitative nature

most of which have a limited degree of reliability. The method of Liebermann-Storch for the identification of rosin is one of the dependable tests, if carried out in the following manner. About 50 milligrams of the resin are dissolved in about 10 c.c. of boiling acetic anhydride. Upon cooling, two c.c. of the solution thus obtained are placed in a white porcelain dish and a drop of sulphuric acid, having a specific weight of 1.53, is added. A fugitive violet color indicates the presence of rosin.

For the purpose of distinguishing gum from wood rosin, ultraviolet light can be used within limits, if care is taken that all visible rays are filtered out. Gum rosin does not light up, whereas wood rosin shows distinct fluorescence. This characteristic difference is carried through into some of the processed resins.

Color reactions have been suggested for the qualitative identification of phenolic resins. For this purpose the resin is gently fused with an equal amount of potassium hydroxide, whereby the phenol component is made water-soluble. The melt, after cooling, is pulverized, extracted with water, the solution filtered and neutralized with mineral acid. The resulting aqueous solution can then be tested for the presence of phenol by the usual color reactions. However, it must be borne in mind that a differentiation between the various types of substituted phenols is not possible.

The identification of maleic resins by chemical means is not possible. Whereas the content of phthalic anhydride in alkyd resins can be determined with reasonable accuracy because the phthalic anhydride can be regained as such from the resin, this procedure is not applicable to maleic or fumaric resins, because both maleic and fumaric acids, differing from phthalic anhydride, lose their identity in the resin-forming process.

Elaborate analytical schemes and systematic procedures have been worked out for the

identification of individual resins

within the whole range of synthetic resins. Applying the suggested analytical procedures to the coating and ink resins under discussion, vague and inconclusive results are obtained, which in no way warrant the considerable time and effort involved in such analyses.

Chapter VI

Influence of Resins on Surface Coatings

The discussion of chemical resin characteristics in the previous chapter, applies to both coating and ink resins. Extending the discussion further to cover physical characteristics of the resins and the practical performance of the resin-oil combinations, it is necessary to consider resins for surface coatings and printing inks separately. The methods of testing physical properties, the viewpoints used in resin evaluation and the manner of practical application is basically different for the two resin groups, as will appear from the detailed comments in this and the chapter following.

PHYSICAL CHARACTERISTICS OF COATING RESINS

The outstanding physical characteristic of coating resins is the melting point. High melting points contribute substantially to the bodying speed of the resins with oil, accelerate the drying of the surface coating and improve the hardness of the film finally formed. Melting points can be increased by proper manufacturing procedures, but not indefinitely, because an upper limit of about 175° to 180° C. is imposed by practical factors in resin production and application.

The melting point

of rosin-based phenolic, maleic and copal-type synthetic resins varies between 140° and 175° C.

As a rule, surface coatings which dry mainly by evaporation of the volatile solvents, do not derive the full benefit from resins with high melting points, because the resins are softened by retained solvent, which may lower their melting points by

20° to 50° C. This softening influence of solvent retention is the same for all resin types under discussion, as explained later on in this chapter. It is noticeably greater, the smaller the relative amount of drying oil or plasticizer present in the surface coating, *i.e.* particularly in cold cuts and quick drying nitrocellulose lacquer combinations. On the other hand, it is negligibly small in baking finishes, where the heat of the drying oven drives off the bulk of the residual solvents.

The melting point of resins is the temperature at which they reach a certain specified degree of fluidity and, therefore, is more appropriately called softening point. It is in no way as distinct as melting points of crystalline organic substances, but nevertheless can be determined as a reproducible constant. The usual procedures for melting point determination employ rising temperature baths, adjusting the speed of heating, or the rate at which the bath temperature increases, so that sufficient time is available for complete transfer of the heat to the resin and to allow the resin sufficient time to start its flow, after its temperature is balanced with that of the bath. If the time factor is given full consideration, reproducible values are obtained, because the particular resin types under consideration in this study, have the same

fluidity temperature coefficient

in the temperature region of their softening point, *i.e.* the rate of flow is influenced by heat in the same way. This important fact is brought out by the experiments described in the following paragraphs. In these tests, samples of high melting rosin-modified phenolics, maleics and copal-type synthetics were investigated in two different procedures.

The first method used the routine mercury method for melting point determination, *i.e.* 3 grams of resin were placed in a ⅝ inch by 6 inch test tube, melted by gentle heat, a thermometer inserted and the resin permitted to cool and solidify. 50 grams of mercury were then placed on top of the

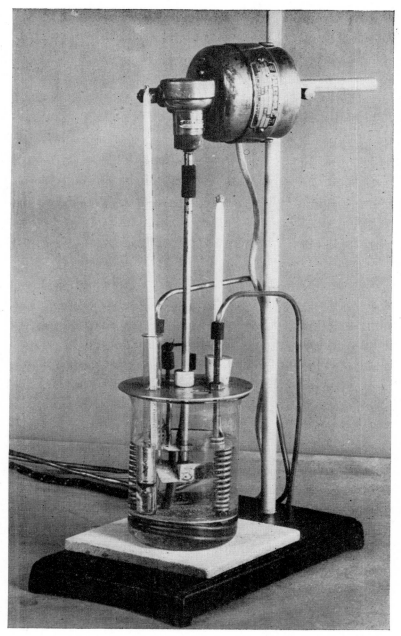

FIGURE 13.   Apparatus for the determination of flow properties
of hard resins.

resin and the test tube was heated in a bath of glycerine. Raising the temperature of the bath 2-3 degrees C. per minute the melting point was registered as the temperature at which the resin started to penetrate the top surface of the mercury.

The second method used a special apparatus which is pictured in *Figure 13*. It consists of a large glycerine bath which can be heated or cooled in a controlled manner, either by an immersion type electrical heater or a cooling coil; both of which are visible in the photograph. Uniform distribution of the temperature within the bath is assured by a motor-driven agitator. The resin samples are heated in the usual test tubes, located in a special tube rack. This apparatus allows a correct control of temperature changes and, being equipped with a thermo regulator, permits the maintenance of constant temperature.

In the particular experiment under discussion, the bath temperature of each resin was adjusted to its individual melting point, determined by the routine mercury method, and kept constant within one degree. This arrangement allowed the temperature rise of the resin sample in the test tube to level off as the temperature approached the melting point thereby giving the resin, while it was in the process of softening, full opportunity to move. In carrying out the experiment, three distinct temperature points could be observed in the movements of resin and mercury. First was observed the point at which the mercury made the incipient slight indentation in the resin layer; second the temperature point at which the mercury started to move down visibly; and finally the point when the resin, in its upward move, reached the surface. Investigated in this way,

all three resins acted alike

showing the first indentation about 40° C. below the orthodox melting point, and the first visible flow about 15° C. below this temperature.

This finding indicates that the rate of flow of the three resin types under discussion is influenced alike by temperature increases. They all become slightly plastic at about 40° C. below the melting point, heavily viscous at about 15° C. below this point and thinly liquid at the traditional melting point.

In addition to the mercury method, the Ball and Ring method or the A.S.T.M. method are reliable and give practically identical values, provided the determination is properly timed. The capillary method, employed in organic chemistry, yields reproducible figures which are usually 10°-15° C. lower than those obtained by the two other methods.

For comparatively soft resins, *i.e.* for resins with a melting point below 125° C. only, the so-called drop method is suitable. It is carried out by dipping the bulb of a thermometer into the fused resin and spreading one-half gram of resin as a uniform layer on the bulb. After placing the thermometer with the resin covered bulb into a test tube, this tube is heated slowly in a bath. The temperature at which the resin starts to fall off the bulb in the form of a drop is recorded as melting point.

The characteristic of the melting point is usually closely related to

viscosity properties

in the way that both move in the same direction. Viscosity characteristics are of great importance for the practical use of the resins in surface coatings, because high viscosities shorten cooking and drying times, and improve film hardness and resistance. Resin viscosities can be considerably modified by proper production methods and resin composition, but its degree can only be increased to a certain point, being about Z_6 in 60% xylol solution on the Gardner scale. If the viscosity is increased beyond this limit, the resins gelatinize in the production kettle and do not dissolve in oil when used in the varnish kettle.

The viscosity of coating resins can be measured under two

different conditions. It can be determined either as the viscosity of the liquified resin at temperatures above the melting point or as the viscosity of the resin in solution at room temperature.

Determinations on the fused resins have to be made at temperatures substantially higher than the melting point, because the viscosity close to this point is influenced too strongly by the factor of temperature to yield sufficiently accurate data, if normal testing equipment is used. It is only at temperatures of 50-100° C. above the melting point that the viscosity-temperature curve flattens out to a line which runs parallel to the temperature abscissa, *i.e.* that the viscosity varies little with temperature changes. The measurement of resin viscosities in liquified condition is not part of the routine laboratory test methods, though a special testing instrument could be devised for this purpose. The viscosity values of fused resins, however, are often gauged when manufacturing the resins in the production kettle by recording the power input required to turn the agitator, as indicated by the ampere-meter of the agitator motor.

For routine laboratory testing the viscosity of coating resins is measured when

dissolved in volatile solvents

usually through making a solution of 60 parts of resin in 40 parts of nitration xylol by boiling under reflux. A tube containing the cold resin solution is compared with the respective tubes of the standard Gardner Bubble Viscometer, and the letter on the Gardner tube which matches exactly the sample, is registered as the viscosity. The temperature of both tubes must be exactly alike, brought about by leaving them together long enough in the same cold-water bath. The solvent used in such determinations must be carefully specified, because the type of solvent greatly influences the viscosity.

To prove the strong influence of the nature of the solvent,

60% solutions in both xylol and mineral spirits of the same resin were prepared. The solution in xylol had a viscosity of K on the Gardner scale, equivalent to about 2.8 poises, the solution in mineral spirits a viscosity of Y, equivalent to about 17.6 poises *i.e.* the viscosity in an aliphatic hydrocarbon, expressed in poises, was about six times heavier than in a coal tar solvent.

The viscosities of the four resin groups discussed in this volume may vary within wide limits. The acid-condensed pure alkyl phenol resins, as well as the alkali-condensed types of both the alkyl and bis phenol variety have low viscosities, with the exception of the high melting acid-condensed para tertiary butyl phenol resin, the xylol solution of which solidifies to a gelatinous mass on cooling and standing. Rosin-modified phenolics and maleics have viscosities which generally vary between K and Z_4 on the Gardner scale. Copal-type synthetics, as a rule, do not exceed a viscosity of Z.

In determining resin viscosities by dissolving them in volatile solvents, it must be taken into consideration that at the comparatively low temperature of the boiling point of the customary solvent, certain resins do not dissolve completely, but show gelatinous particles which only swell in the solvent and do not contribute to the viscosity of the solution, thereby yielding results which are not accurate. This condition is found particularly in resin types of excessively high body. Sometimes their viscosity is more accurately measured when dissolved in heated oil, whereby the gelatinous parts might go into solution.

The viscosity of resin solutions in volatile solvents depends, in a very characteristic way, on the

degree of concentration of the resin.

This interesting relationship is pictured in the graph of *Figure 14*. The three curves show the relationship of the viscosities of solutions of modified phenolics, modified maleics and copal-type synthetics in mineral spirits, to the concentration of the resins in the solutions.   In order to obtain reliable and easily measurable viscosity values, concentrations were chosen to yield figures within the range of 1 and 150 poises, and the

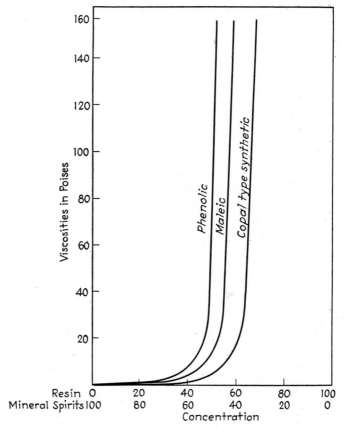

FIGURE 14.   Relationship of resin concentration to viscosity of solution.

concentrations were not lowered to the point that precipitation of the resins took place.   Viscosities were expressed in poises, instead of in terms of the Gardner scale, in order to base the curves on absolute flow values.

The illustration shows a perfect analogy of the curves at low viscosity values and a complete parallelity at high viscosities, proving that the viscosity of phenolics, maleics and copal-type synthetics is governed in the same manner by the factor of resin concentration. None of the resin groups shows any irregularity through one class losing viscosity fast on thinning, and another group being reduced slowly in viscosity by the addition of thinner.

It appears, furthermore, that all resin concentrations under 30% have extremely low viscosities, providing the resin solution will stand thinning to this point without precipitation. Heavy viscosities of more than 20 poises, *i.e.* about Z on the Gardner scale, are reached at concentrations which differ characteristically for the three resin classes. This concentration is 62% for copal-type synthetics, 54% for maleic resins and amounts to 46% for modified phenolics.

It is possible that the comparatively high value found for copal-type synthetics and the relatively lower values found for modified maleics and phenolics are a result of the extreme molecular homogeneity of copal-type synthetics and their lack of oversized molecules, which may be present in the other resin types.

In addition to the characteristics of melting points and viscosity, the

relationship of resins and solvents

plays a role in varnish technology in many different ways. The solubility of the resins themselves governs the production of cold cuts, as used for varnishes, lacquers, and synthetic finishes, whereas the solubility of the resins in oil and the solubility of the resin-oil combination is the base for oleoresinous varnishes generally. As a rule, the solubility characteristics of the resin proper are conveyed to their combination with oil, the degree of solubility being augmented by an increase of the oil portion in such combinations.

The dissolving of resins in strong solvents presents no problems. Important practical questions, however, arise when the role of weak or non-solvents is to be considered. These questions are complicated by the tendency of some resins to crystallize and by the various degrees of their compatibility with other substances. Further problems are added by the peculiar resin property of retaining volatile solvents after the resin solution has dried to a solid thin layer.

Coal tar and hydrogenated hydrocarbons, and most of the strong organic solvents, produce perfect solutions of all coating resins under discussion, bearing in mind that perfect solubility is characterized by the fact that the resin solution can be diluted infinitely without precipitation or crystallization of the resin.

Aliphatic hydrocarbons with

Kauri butanol values

of 38-40 possess perfect solvent power for only a limited number of resins, such as alkali-condensed straight phenolics, modified alkyl phenol resins, certain maleics and copal-type synthetics. The solvency decreases rapidly with the Kauri butanol value of the solvent. Therefore, cuts of hydrocarbons with a Kauri butanol value of 28 to 34 have a much weaker solvent power, producing perfect solutions only in exceptional cases as, for instance, with straight amyl phenol resins or with highly degraded copal-type synthetics.

For economic reasons, all resin or resin-oil solutions in volatile solvents contain weak solvents or solvents which possess no solvent power when used alone. The question of the tolerance of resin solutions to such additions, as governed by the resinous component, is therefore of great practical importance. Besides,

tolerance values

supply a good measure for the degree of resin solubility.

The tolerance of surface coating resins for weak or non-solvents is determined by a simple method of titration. 10 grams of a solution of 60 grams of resin in 40 grams of xylol are titrated with mineral spirits of a Kauri butanol value of 39, until a distinct permanent haze appears in the solution. The number of c.c. of mineral spirits required to reach this point is recorded as the mineral spirits tolerance.

The tolerance values of the coating resins under discussion vary within wide limits. For the pure phenolics they are usually high, even infinite, because of complete solubility in mineral spirits. The tolerance values of modified phenolics vary between 15 and infinity, depending on several factors. For instance, alkyl phenol resins have higher tolerance than bis phenol resins. The tolerance changes with the type and amount of esterifying alcohol, decreases with increasing resin viscosity and becomes greater when the resins are subjected to the maturing procedure. The tolerance of maleic resins also may vary within wide limits, depending on similar factors, such as resin composition, viscosity and state of maturing, as in the case of phenolics. Copal-type synthetics are distinguished by high mineral spirits tolerance, which seldom declines below 30 c.c. and often exceeds 50 c.c.

Whereas the solubility in mineral spirits is a good criterion with which to judge the suitability of varnish resins, the

solubility in alcohol

is helpful in evaluating the usefulness of lacquer resins. The degree of alcohol solubility is determined by titrating the 60% resin solution, previously described, with ethyl alcohol until the point of cloud formation. It is necessary to use for this purpose absolute alcohol, because the titration values are influenced substantially by the presence of small amounts of water, ethyl acetate and other substances. Using 10 c.c. of the resin solution, very small values of about one c.c. are found for modified phenolics, double the amount, *i.e.*, about two c.c. for modified maleics, and figures higher than ten c.c. for non-esterified modified phenolics. Complete solubility in alcohol is limited to a few highly acid maleic and fumaric resins.

Certain rosin types, ester gums, non-matured phenolics, and high acid maleics, show a tendency to crystallize from straight solutions or cold cuts in solvents or solvent mixtures of low solvent power. The trend to crystal formation is the more pronounced the lower the molecular weight of the resinous substance and the stronger its internal tendency of orientation. The powerful forces of internal orientation can be made visible

FIGURE 15.   Example of molecular orientation in a crystal.

under the polarizing microscope. As an example, *Figure* 15 shows very spectacular orientation within a crystal of trional. Under the same conditions, a colloidal polymer, with no internal orientation, yields a uniformly black picture, while the highly orientated trional crystal shows the internal forces with amazing clarity in every detail.

The tendency of resins to

crystallize out of varnishes or lacquers

is greatly reduced by the presence of colloidal matter, such as bodied oils or plasticizers. The two photomicrographs shown in *Figure 16* demonstrate very spectacularly how colloidal matter interferes with crystallization. Both represent the same material—in the left hand picture crystallizing from a pure solvent, in the right hand picture crystallizing from the same solvent containing colloidal matter. The pure sol-

Figure 16. Colloidal matter interfering with crystallization.

vent yields well defined, long crystalline needles, whereas the contaminated liquid yields chainlike aggregates, which are only vaguely orientated.

Closely connected with resin solubility is the question of the compatibility of resins with other substances, such as nitrocellulose, ethyl cellulose, waxes, mazein, D.D.T., etc. Clarity in solution is no measure for compatibility, because clear solutions, containing both resins and foreign additions, can be prepared, in most cases, if strong solvents are used. It is the clarity of the dried film, containing the resin combination after the volatile solvents have evaporated, that shows the true degree of compatibility. As a rule, only perfectly clear films are considered to indicate satisfactory compatability.

The lower the

compatibility of a resin

the larger is the portion of the admixture of resin necessary to avoid the formation of a cloudy film. Applying this rule to the important relationship of maleic resins and nitrocellulose, it can be stated that perfectly compatible, low melting and low viscous maleics will give clear films with cotton to resin ratios as low as $1:\frac{1}{2}$; whereas, some of the poorly compatible, high melting and very viscous maleics yield clear films only with cotton to resin ratios as high as $1:2$. Pentaerythritol-containing maleics have a particularly low degree of compatibility with nitrocellulose. In all cases, the degree of compatibility depends to some extent on the type of solvents used, because, in spite of their volatility, substantial amounts of the solvents are retained by the dried film and make the film-forming materials more compatible.

To cite a few examples of unusual compatibility, it may be mentioned that soft maleics are compatible with ethyl cellulose and vinyl compounds, certain diethylene glycol rosin esters with mazein, and that the acid-condensed, straight amyl phenol resin is compatible with normal and microcrystalline paraffin wax.

Of considerable practical interest is the compatibility of surface coating resins with D.D.T. It has been found that only the D.D.T. that separates from the surface coating material and works its way to the surface of the film, appearing there in the form of microscopic crystals, has any insecticidal effect. The coating resins, here under consideration, do not favor this effect, because they are completely compatible with D.D.T. and do not promote its separation from the surface coating.

When solvents of resin or resin-oil solutions evaporate from a surface coating, a thin layer remains, which

retains considerable amounts of solvents.

This quantity is usually much higher and it remains much longer in the film than might be expected. How firmly volatile solvents are sometimes retained is known in analytical practice from the difficulty experienced in completely driving off the volatile solvents from oleo-resinous varnishes.

Residual solvents greatly influence the mechanical properties of the dried film as it appears, for instance, from the role played by retained solvents in undercoats and sanding sealers. Their influence consists mainly in a considerable lowering of the melting point of the non-volatile part, which can well be visualized by recording the decrease of melting points of straight resins due to the addition of a small amount of solvent. *Table 12* shows the melting points of various resin types in pure form and after the incorporation of 10% mineral oil, which was used for this purpose because it could, in all cases, be homogeneously combined with the various resins.

Table 12. Influence of Solvent Retention on Melting Points of Resins

Resin Type	*Melting Points of*		*Lowering of Melting Point*
	Resin Proper	*Resin Fused with 10% Mineral Oil*	
Pure acid-condensed butyl phenol resin	130° C.	90° C.	40° C.
Rosin-modified butyl phenol resin	170° C.	130° C.	40° C.
Rosin-modified bis phenol resin	155° C.	115° C.	40° C.
High melting maleic resin	150° C.	110° C.	40° C.
Medium-hard maleic resin	135° C.	95° C.	40° C.
Copal-type synthetic resin	140° C.	100° C.	40° C.

The chart proves the surprising fact that the lowering of the resin melting point, due to the retained solvent, is the same for all resins concerned, regardless of composition and degree of hardness. It also shows that the softening effect of retained solvent is much larger than usually expected, amounting to a lowering of the melting point of about 40° C. for 10% of residual solvent. This strangely depressing action explains the importance that the producer of surface coatings attaches to the question of solvent retention.

The degree of solvent retention depends on the properties of both the solvents and the non-volatile material. The role of resins in the non-volatile portion is of interest in the present discussion. Both the speed of solvent evaporation and the amount of solvent retained are measured by the following simple method: 0.5 gram of a resin solution containing 30% resin is weighed into an aluminum dish of 75 millimeter diameter and spread out in a uniformly thin layer. The dishes are kept at room temperature in a dustfree and draft protected place and weighed at regular intervals.

This method was used to determine the

speed of solvent evaporation

and the degree of solvent retention of resins representing the five groups discussed in this book. *Table 13* records the results obtained from xylol solutions of a straight and modified phenolic, a maleic and a copal-type synthetic, the samples being weighed after intervals of one and two hours, one day, one week and one month.

All resins showed practically the same speed of evaporation

Table 13. Speed of Solvent Release from Various Resins

Resin Type	Parts of Xylon Retained in 100 Parts of Resin After:				
	One Hour	Two Hours	One Day	One Week	One Month
Pure acid-condensed butyl phenol resin	80	25	13	13	13
Rosin-modified bis phenol resin	60	20	13	13	13
High melting maleic resin	50	20	13	13	13
Copal-type synthetic resin	70	20	13	13	13

and the same amount of solvent finally retained in the resin film. The percentage of residue did not change noticeably after one day and did not decrease further over a long period of time, obviously forming part of the film. In spite of the comparatively high volatility of a solvent like xylol, the surprisingly high amount of 13% remained in the film after one month. In the case of less volatile solvents the amount of residual solvent is even greater.

As it appears from the data previously given, solvent retention is not a characteristic which differentiates the various resin groups. Solvent retention or solvent release in daily practice, however, is considered to have an important bearing on lacquer resins, particularly maleics, because it is supposed to govern the

sanding properties of the resins.

Table 14 records the speed of evaporation and the amount of retained solvents for a hard and a soft lacquer maleic resin which, according to trade practice, differ distinctly in sanding characteristics. Measurements were made with solutions of 25% resin in a mixture of equal parts of butyl acetate, alcohol and toluol.

Table 14. Solvent Retention of Lacquer Maleic Resins

Solution Used	Time of Weighing After Flow Out	Amount of Retained Solvent Expressed in Per Cent of Resin for a	
		Good Sanding Hard Maleic M.P. 155° C.	Poor Sanding Soft Maleic M.P. 130° C.
	15 minutes	65%	67%
	30 minutes	41%	44%
25% resin in mixture of equal parts of butyl acetate, toluol, alcohol	45 minutes	30%	31%
	60 minutes	29%	29%
	2 hours	25%	25%
	6 hours	20%	20%

The values obtained and recorded in the chart were identical, within experimental limits, for both types of maleic resins, proving that both resins release solvents with the same speed and finally retain the same amount of solvent. Considering the sanding properties of a lacquer as a function of the resin present, it follows that sanding properties, traditionally considered to be governed by solvent retention, actually are a function of the melting point of the resin.

The parallelism, which the various resin types show in their tolerance for solvents of low potency, extends to the degree of their solubility in drying oils, *i.e.* the better their solubility is in weak solvents, the greater their solubility in oils. The relative

solubility of resins in oil

is defined as the minimum temperature at which resin and oil form a perfect combination. For this determination one part of resin is heated with two parts of varnish linseed oil, increasing the temperature 5° C. per minute. The clearing point or temperature of clarification is recorded as the temperature at which a small sample taken from the batch stays clear on cooling. The clearing points vary within wide limits, *i.e.* between 150° C. and 300° C., low temperatures of clarification indicating soluble resins with high mineral spirits tolerance and high temperatures showing resins which are difficult to dissolve and which have little tolerance for mineral spirits.

The survey in *Table 15* demonstrates the solubility characteristics under discussion. Resins with a clearing point under 175° C. unite completely with oils by cold mixing without, or with the help of, a common solvent. Resins with clearing points of 180-210° C. dissolve immediately in oil when reaching this temperature. Resins with higher clarification temperatures require some time for perfect dissolution and pass through a stage of incomplete solution during which the batch is clear only while hot, but becomes cloudy on cooling.

Table 15. Oil Solubility of Resins Expressed in Clearing Temperatures and Compared to Mineral Spirits Tolerance

Resin Type	*Clearing Point*	*Mineral Spirits Tolerance*
Acid-condensed amyl phenol resin	150° C.	Infinite
Alkali-condensed butyl phenol resin	160° C.	Infinite
Pale copal-type synthetic	170° C.	200 c.c.
Acid-condensed butyl phenol resin	220° C.	100 c.c.
Rosin-modified alkyl phenol resin	230° C.	50 c.c.
High solubility type maleic resin	240° C.	40 c.c.
Rosin-modified bis phenol resin	260° C.	25 c.c.
Low solubility type maleic resin	280° C.	15 c.c.

In the case of resins difficult to dissolve, the clearing point moves upward with increasing amounts of oils, to a point where some of these resins will not form clear solutions, even at excessively high temperatures, if more than two parts of oil to one of resin are used. In such cases, the combination has to be carried out in steps. The total amount of oil is added in several separate parts, every addition being made only after the previous one is clearly dissolved. Clearing points also move upwards with the viscosity of the oil used, as is to be expected.

RESIN-OIL COMBINATIONS IN COATINGS

The chemical and physical characteristics of the resins, previously discussed, are carried over into the resin-oil combinations which form the base for surface coatings, and such characteristics influence the properties of coatings in many different ways. They are important for bodying speed, the maximum obtainable viscosity, the peculiarity of after-bodying and the pigment stability. They influence the spreading, drying, and decorative characteristics of surface layers. They govern the mechanical properties of hardness and flexibility, and have a decided influence on the chemical resistance and weatherproofness of surface coatings.

Under practical conditions, resin-oil combinations are prepared by fusing the two ingredients together until a physical mixture is obtained. When such physical resin-oil combinations are subjected to further heat treatment, the viscosity is increased at a speed which depends both on the type of the oil and the class of resin used. Normal coating resins, with few exceptions, accelerate

the bodying speed

of all drying oils. One important exception is the delaying action of highly acid phenolic resins on the gelling of China wood oil or oiticica oil.

As a rule, the accelerating effect of resins on the polymerization of oils is less pronounced with quick bodying oils and, differences in this characteristic, therefore, can best be measured with slow bodying oils such as linseed oil. A simple method for the determination of bodying speed is the following: one part of resin is heated with two parts of unbodied varnish linseed oil in 50 minutes to 305° C. and is held at this temperature with exact, preferably thermostatic, control, until a sample, dissolved in the same weight of mineral spirits, shows a viscosity of D on the Gardner viscosity scale. The time of heating at 305° C., required to reach this viscosity, is recorded as bodying speed.

In practical varnish making the air comes into contact with the surface of the resin-oil mixture and accelerates the bodying speed. The air, therefore, should not be excluded in the laboratory determination of the bodying time. To obtain comparable results in this test, the same amounts of material and the same equipment must be used in all cases.

Another characteristic of resin-oil combinations is the viscosity reached immediately before gelation. The

maximum viscosity that can be obtained

by bodying resin and oil together without the formation of insoluble gelatinous particles varies greatly with the type of resin and is determined during the same test used for the determination of the bodying speed.

The two property characteristics of bodying speed and maximum viscosity obtainable were demonstrated with a series of four different varnishes, based on a rosin-modified phenolic,

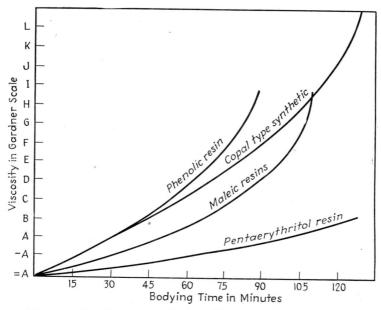

FIGURE 17. Increase of viscosity with bodying time.

a modified maleic, a copal-type synthetic resin and a rosin-pentaerythritol ester. The varnishes were made with one part of resin and two parts of unbodied varnish linseed oil, the bodying carried out under equal conditions at close to 305° C. or 580° F. Samples were withdrawn every 15 minutes and viscosities were determined.

The interesting figures obtained are recorded in the graph of *Figure 17* in which the viscosity values are plotted against bodying time. The

curves are very characteristic

for the performance of the four resin classes in the varnish kettle. During the first 45 minutes phenolics and copal-type synthetics body with about the same speed, with maleics bodying distinctly slower and pentaerythritol esters remaining far behind the other resins.

During the next 45 minutes the phenolic varnish bodies rapidly and gelatinizes suddenly, after reaching a viscosity of I, this behavior being indicated in the graph by the steep ascent of the curve and its abrupt ending. During the second 45 minutes' cooking period, the copal-type synthetic continues to body in a normal and uniform manner, whereas the maleic varnish, still considerably slower than the phenolic varnish, shows a decided tendency to increase its bodying speed. After 100 minutes of bodying time, its viscosity increase becomes extremely rapid, leading to a sudden gelation of the batch.

The copal-type synthetic varnish continues its steady and very substantial increase in viscosity, showing no signs of gelation within the time limit of this experiment. This performance proves clearly that copal-type synthetic varnishes can be bodied, without gelation, to much higher viscosities than either phenolic or maleic varnishes.

During all this time, the pentaerythritol ester varnish has increased its body only very moderately, as indicated by the nearly horizontal direction of the curve.

As it appears from the curves in *Figure 17*, the bodying process in the varnish kettle is closely related to the characteristics of the resins. More details on these relationships are given in *Table 16*, showing how bodying speed and maximum obtainable viscosity are dependent on resin acidity, viscosity, solubility and reactivity. Data are given for the three resin groups of phenolics, maleics and copal types, selecting within each group at least two distinctly different members. Acid values and viscosities of the resins are expressed in the usual terms. The oil solubility is expressed as the temperature of clarification as previously described; the degree of oil reactivity of the resins as established by composition and performance.

Table 16. Resin Influence on Bodying Process in Varnish Kettle

Resins	Acid Value of Resin	Viscosity of Resin as Gardner Scale Letter	Oil Solubility of Resin Expressed as Clearing Point	Degree of Oil Reactivity of Resin	Bodying Time of Resin Oil Combination	Maximum Viscosity of Resin Oil Combination in Solution
Low phenol content modified phenolic	18	X	240° C.	medium	90 min.	K
High phenol content modified phenolic	18	Z_3	260° C.	high	60 min.	I
High phenol content phenolic, non-esterified	115	Z	230° C.	high	120 min.	O
Low hydroxyl content copal-type synthetic	15	K	180° C.	medium	80 min.	P
High hydroxyl content copal-type synthetic	5	N	180° C.	high	60 min.	P
Low maleic content maleic resin	30	F	220° C.	very low	120 min.	K
High maleic content maleic resin	30	U	280° C.	low	90 min.	I

A number of interesting conclusions regarding

the resin influence on the bodying process

can be drawn from *Table 16.*

The bodying time increases with the acidity of the resin, as shown by comparing the figures for an unesterified phenolic with those of an esterified phenolic, or by comparing the values of a low acid copal-type synthetic with those of a high acid copal-type synthetic. Bodying time is not influenced by the oil solubility of the resin, but depends to some extent on the initial viscosity of the resin, as evidenced by a comparison of a low viscosity with a high viscosity phenolic.

The paramount factor governing the bodying speed of resin oil combinations is the degree of oil reactivity of the resins. The very low, or nonexistent, reactivity of rosin esterified with glycerol or pentaerythritol, requires many hours to gain sufficient viscosity. The weak chemical activity of low maleic content maleic resins causes them to body very slowly with oils. The high maleic content maleic, which necessarily possesses better oil reactivity, bodies considerably faster. The two resin groups of phenolics and copal-type synthetics, both of which possess a medium to high degree of oil reactivity, body with considerable speed, depending on the number of reactive phenolic or alcoholic hydroxyl groups present.

The interesting field of the oil reactivity of resins can be investigated further by a systematic study of the

changes in molecular weights

during the bodying process, using the methods for the determination of molecular sizes described in a previous chapter. From a preliminary survey of molecular weights in this field, it appears that polymerized linseed oil, immediately before entering the gelatinous stage, has a molecular weight of 2400, *i.e.* is in a state in which two to three molecules are agglomerated into one aggregate. It also is found that heat bodied combinations of resins and oils which, before the combining process, possess individual molecular weights of 1400, show weights of 2200, indicating a considerable molecular association during the bodying process.

The maximum viscosity obtainable in oleo-resinous varnishes does not depend on the resin viscosity proper, as evidenced by a comparison of low and high viscosity phenolics and maleics in *Table 16*. The maximum viscosity is distinctly influenced by the acidity of the resin, high acid values permitting the production of higher viscosities. The performance of the non-esterified phenolic clearly demonstrates this fact. Another factor which plays a role in establishing the upper limit of varnish viscosity is the solubility of the resins in oil, the result being that the better the oil solubility of a resin, the higher is the viscosity obtainable in varnish cooking without gelation. For this reason, the copal-type synthetics, which have a very low clarification temperature in oil, can be cooked with oils to much higher viscosities than phenolics or maleics which do not clear easily in oil. The data of *Table 16* prove these points.

The degree of oil reactivity of the resins does not seem to have a pronounced bearing on the maximum viscosity obtainable in varnish cooking. Oil reactivity, however, exerts an influence on

the after-bodying of varnishes

i.e. their viscosity increase, occurring when they are stored for several weeks at room temperature. After-bodying, once started, usually continues, and a strong viscosity increase, observed after four weeks foretells, as a rule, complete gelation after another four weeks. After-bodying is always greatly accelerated by the presence of driers. This factor was eliminated in comparative testing of the after-bodying of varnishes by using the same amount of drier metals in all cases.

Observations made of the varnishes produced in preparing the data of *Table 16* threw an interesting light on the inner relationship of after-bodying of the varnishes and the oil reactivity of the resin present in the varnish. It appeared that varnishes, on the base of maleic resins with little oil reactivity, showed strong tendency to after-body, whereas varnishes, based on phenolics and copal-type synthetics with pronounced oil reactivity, had no such tendency. In accordance with this observation, as a rule, strong after-bodying is found in varnishes which contain heavily prebodied oils.

When oils are bodied to high viscosities before they are combined with the resin, they lose much of their own reactive capability, with the result that resin and oil remain chemically inert in the combining process, yielding a varnish with strong tendency to after-bodying.

Another factor governing the after-bodying of resin-oil vehicles, as seen from the resin angle, is the presence of over-polymerized parts in many of the high viscosity resins. Though a large portion of these gelatinous parts is degelled in the varnish-cooking process, a substantial part sometimes remains.

The viscosity increase of the resin-oil-solvent system with time, *i.e.* the after-bodying of oleo-resinous varnishes on storage, is also closely connected with

the pigment reactivity

of the varnish vehicles. If they show a strong tendency to viscosity increase, they will also quickly gelatinize with pigments. Accordingly, the pigment stability of phenolics and copal-type synthetics is superior to that of maleics.

If surface reactive types of pigments are used, the over-polymerized, labile particles present in a state of suspended gelation in some resins, particularly in certain maleics, play a part in this reaction. If basic pigments are used, the acidity of the resins is an influence. However, in the latter case, it has to be considered that the average enamel vehicle consists of only about one-sixth of resin, whereby the initial resin acidity is reduced to one-sixth in the vehicle. A resin with an acid value of 30, for instance, will act as a material with an acid value of 5, which is fully within safe limits. In addition, it must be kept in mind that the reactivity of resinous acidic substances is much less pronounced than that of fatty acids and, for this reason, the pigment reactivity of resin oil combinations depends little on resin acidity and is dominated by the fatty acids of the oily component.

Drier metals accelerate livering with pigments in the same way that they promote after-bodying of the unpigmented vehicle, a consideration which is of importance when the relationship of resin properties and pigment stability is studied.

The pigment stability of the resin-oil-solvent system seems to be related to the

phenomenon of skinning.

If the stability with pigments is lacking, surface skinning usually becomes obvious. This observation leads to the conclusion that the same resin properties which cause livering, will accelerate skinning. Accordingly, the tendency to skin formation is, apart from drier influence, a function of the acidity, the oil reactivity and the molecular state of the resins The influence of the acidity is minor, being overshadowed and obscured by the effect of fatty acids. The favorable influence of pronounced oil reactivity and the lack of gelatinous high molecular parts in copal-type synthetics explains the non-skinning properties of these resin types.

Most coating resins have the ultimate purpose of promoting the quick formation of a glossy film with mechanical and chemical resistance. The role played by resins in film formation has to do with the application and spreading of the material and the phase of the drying of the thin wet film; it has considerable bearing on the decorative and protective properties of the dried film.

The spreading characteristics of surface coating materials, as expressed by their brushability or their workability in spraying or dipping, are little influenced by the resins present in the coatings and depend largely on the other ingredients. As a rule, only the viscosity characteristics of the resins have a bearing on the

workability of clear surface coating materials

because their peculiarities are carried over into the resin-oil-solvent combination. In certain cases, high viscosity resins seem to produce thixotropy in paints and enamels, *i.e.* the ability to become more free-flowing when moved mechanically, with the result that they impart easy brushability to otherwise too viscous paints and enamels. They may also help in preventing sagging and other irregularities, such as the formation of curtains, when a finish is applied to vertical surfaces.

The second step in film formation, *i.e.* the drying process, is decidedly influenced by the resins present, regardless as to whether or not the drying is due mainly to oxidation, as in ordinary coatings, or to polymerization, as in baking finishes. Resins may either retard or accelerate the film formation.

Retardation of drying

occurs in relatively few cases. Certain phenol resins may contain free phenols which retard drying. The retarding action is known from phenols, such as resorcinol or beta-naphthol, occasionally used as antioxidants in paint making. As explained in the chapter on phenolic resins, the formaldehyde condensates of certain phenol types have a decidedly antidrying influence even if there is no free phenol present, their retarding influence becoming particularly apparent with soft oils such as linseed. Another cause for delayed drying is the precipitation of drier metals as insoluble salts, which destroys their efficiency. It occurs with certain maleic resins containing free succinic acid, which precipitates, as succinates, the drier metals, especially cobalt and lead, and it also happens with certain pure phenolics containing acids, such as phosphoric, which had served as catalyst during the production of the resin.

In the majority of cases, resins have an

accelerating effect on the drying

of the wet surface coating film. To demonstrate this effect, various resins were incorporated into varnishes, and the time to reach complete tack-freeness was determined. The varnishes were made as follows: one part of resin was heated with two parts of *Z* body linseed oil in 50 minutes to 300° C. and held there to reach an *H* viscosity, after thinning with three parts of mineral spirits. To the solution, 0.1% cobalt and 1.0% lead, figured on the oil portion, were added as driers. The dying conditions of temperature, light and humidity were identical for all varnishes. The resulting drying times were the following:

Copal-type synthetic resin	*4 hours*
Non-esterified modified phenolic	*5 hours*
Rosin-modified bis phenol resin	*6 hours*
Rosin-modified maleic resin	*7 hours*
Rosin-modified alkyl phenol resin	*8 hours*

The degree of acceleration in drying speed due to the incorporation of resin into the oil can be easily judged in these examples from the fact that under identical conditions the pure oil component, when drying alone, showed a drying time of ten hours.

The speeding up of drying has both mechanical and chemical causes. A purely physical acceleration of the drying and hardening process takes place, because the hard resin itself, representing the solid phase, favors solidification of the film. The drying speed increases with the percentage of resin present and is accelerated pronouncedly by the use of higher-melting resins. Soft resins have little effect on drying speed, hard resins are very efficient in this respect.

An acceleration of the drying process due to chemical causes takes place in the presence of free resin acidity. A chemical explanation for this peculiar phenomenon is difficult to find but it is a fact that, for instance, unesterified modified phenolics cause considerably faster drying than the esterified types.

Where a strong oil reactivity of the resin exists, its influence on drying speed manifests itself very distinctly for the reason that a chemically uniform material has better film-forming properties than a physical mixture. Accordingly, the highly reactive copal-type synthetics dry quicker and harder than the low reactive maleics.

There are some significant exceptions to this rule in the field of phenolics, because of the varying drying acceleration properties of individual phenol derivatives. Pure para phenyl phenol resins dry considerably faster with soft oils than do pure para tertiary alkyl phenol resins, although there is no difference in the oil reactivity of the two resins. Modified alkyl phenol resins dry slower with linseed oil than do modified bis phenol resins, in spite of the even higher oil reactivity of the former.

The gloss of dried surface coating films is based on a variety of factors, among which the amount and type of their resin content is paramount; in fact, resins are indispensable components in the production of glossy coatings.

The resin influence on gloss

is governed by a few simple rules. For a precise study of gloss conditions the Hunter reflectometer was used, as pictured in *Figure 18*. On the left hand side is seen the reflectometer proper, which is based on a photoelectric cell. It registers the amount of reflected light by means of a galvanometer, shown on the right hand side of the picture.

On the whole, gloss increases with the relative amount of resin present and with the degree of polymerization of the resin-oil cook. Accordingly, as a rule, short oil varnishes have better gloss than long oil varnishes, and varnishes that have been bodied for a longer period of time show a higher gloss than those which have been incompletely heat-combined or have been bodied only for a short period of time. Because the degree of the viscosity of oleo-resinous varnish bases is increased by resins of initially high viscosity and pronounced oil reactivity, the latter two resin characteristics influence indirectly the degree of gloss.

Beyond this no individually different effects of resins on gloss development can be noticed. Gloss is independent of

FIGURE 18.   The Hunter reflectometer.

the chemical nature of the resin and, therefore, the same degree of gloss can be obtained with any of the four resin groups under discussion. Gloss of surface coatings is also independent of the refractive index of the resin used in the oil combination, a correlation which is sometimes assumed to exist. For instance, ester gums or modified phenolics, which have relatively low refractive indices varying between 1.53 and 1.56, yield surface coatings of practically the same gloss as coumarone resins or para phenyl phenol resins, which have considerably higher refractive indices varying between 1.63 and 1.66, evidencing the fact that no relationship exists between gloss and refractive index.

Of even greater importance than the resin influence on the gloss of surface coatings is their influence on

the question of film resistance.

Surface coating films, after drying, are exposed to a number of destructive forces and over a period of time are destroyed by oxidation, hydrolysis and mechanical actions. For the production of durable films, therefore, the use of resins which are resistant to oxygen, to water and to physical stress and strain, is required. To form a clear opinion of the role played by the resins under consideration, a detailed discussion of these three destructive factors is necessary.

After a film has been formed in the drying process with the help of oxygen, the dried film continues to oxidize and this

oxidation finally destroys the coating.

The first sign of incipient destruction of an oleo-resinous surface coating film due to oxidation is a darkening of its color. The discoloration is caused mainly by the darkening of the oily component, but the resinous portion also plays a part. On exposure to oxidizing influences in thin layers, particularly if oxidation is accelerated by sun irradiation, the various resins change their color in different ways. Maleic resins undergo relatively little darkening; dark colored copal-type synthetics sometimes bleach out considerably; modified phenolics show decided discoloration; and pure phenolics display strong darkening tendencies.

The oxidation of oleo-resinous surface coating films, which manifests itself in their color changes, is accompanied by an increase of the acidity of such films, which can be determined by extracting the dried film with proper solvents, and taking the acid value of the extract. The increase in acidity is a convenient measure of the progress of oxidation.

In this way, it can be shown that oxidation is delayed by synthetic resins in proportion to the amount of resin added to the oil, and in accordance with their degree of chemical stability and their ability of chemically reacting with the oil. Highly reactive resins, which continue to react with the oil portion when applied in surface coatings, particularly when subjected to baking temperatures in heat drying, delay oxidation most effectively, eventually stopping the oxidation process entirely.

The destructive action of oxygen on resin-oil combinations is intensified by

the hydrolyzing effect of water

in vapor or liquid form. Water resistance can be measured in a scientifically correct way by establishing stress-strain curves for detached films in a tensile test apparatus under varying conditions of water influence. For evaluating the important part played by resins in the waterproofness of films, it is customary to compare the performance of the dried surface coatings on test panels, prepared by the standard test methods described in many specifications. After immersing the panels for 24 hours in cold water, one hour in boiling water, and 30 minutes in 2% alkali solution respectively, the immersed part of the film is examined for whitening, blooming, blistering, softening and loss of adhesion. Such a practical test supplies a more descriptive picture of hydrolytic resistance than scientific measurements of individual characteristics, because waterproofness is of a highly involved nature.

Water not only acts on the surface of the coatings, but also penetrates into the layer itself and infiltrates between the coating and its support. Film deterioration by hydrolysis, especially on metals, is accelerated by salt solutions more than by pure water, because they stimulate electrical activity. Another factor intensifying the action of water, is the presence of free acids, which tend to accelerate the splitting of resinous and oily ester compounds. An action even more destructive than that of free acids is exerted by solutions containing free alkali, including soap solutions.

The hard synthetic resins discussed in this technological study improve the water resistance of oleo-resinous films. The degree of improvement increases with the relative amount of resin present and changes with the type of resin used. Pure phenolics increase water resistance most efficiently, closely followed by rosin-modified alkyl phenol resins. Copal-type synthetics and modified phenolics have a slightly lower waterproofing effect than the groups previously mentioned, whereas maleics are considerably less efficient.

The waterproofing effect of resins is due to a number of different causes. All resins in question are of a hard and non-porous type. When combined with oil, they convey an adequate part of these properties to the oil which, as such, dries to a soft and porous film. Thereby, the resins reduce the tendency of the oil film to swell under the influence of water, and decrease the permeability of the film for water in liquid or vapor form. Thus they prevent the water from reaching vulnerable points within or beneath the surface coating where the destructive forces of hydrolysis attack.

All resins under discussion possess a very high degree of resistance against hydrolysis or saponification. As a rule, the waterproofing effect is directly proportional to

their saponification resistance

which increases in the sequence of maleics, copal-type synthetics and phenolics. When combined with oil, the resins impart a large part of their inherent water resistance to the oil, which in itself possesses only a small fraction of the water resistance of that of resins.

Water resistance of a film is directly proportional to its alkali resistance, when the film material is relatively neutral. If free acids are present, as is generally the case in the aged films, the resistance to alkali is largely reduced, while the resistance to water is much less affected. This is due to the fact that the alkali forms soaps with the free acids which emulsify the film material and thereby facilitate the hydrolysis.

Many of the coating resins possess the capability of chemically reacting with oils, thereby forming molecular complexes which have a higher resistance to hydrolysis, swelling and permeation than the merely physical mixture of the two components. Accordingly, the waterproofing effect of resins is a direct function of the degree of their oil reactivity; consequently it is very pronounced in phenolics and copal-type synthetics, but not in maleics.

The reinforcement due to resins observed in clear surface coatings is also found in pigmented finishes as paints and enamels, and is particularly pronounced in pigmented coatings which contain such basic pigments as lead or zinc oxide. In these cases, the acidity of the vehicles, part of which is due to the resins present, causes reactions of the basic pigments in the dried surface coating layer. Gradually a halo of metal soap is formed around each pigment particle. The reaction is slow, because it occurs among and within solid phases. However, after several weeks the soap crystals may have grown to considerable length, penetrating the entire paint layer.

Figure 19 demonstrates this condition clearly. It is a microphotograph taken with polarized light and a magnification of 400 times, of a red-lead particle, embedded in a dried oleoresinous film, which contains a resin of high acid value. It is evident from the picture that the lead soap needles, surrounding the red lead particle, make

the film structure more coherent and dense,

thereby protecting it physically against the destructive attacks of water or chemicals in their various forms.

This sort of protection is of particular importance for anti-corrosive finishes, more specifically for rust preventive coat-

FIGURE 19.

Needles of lead soap crystals growing on a particle of red lead.

ings on iron. *Figure 20* is a photograph in color descriptive of corrosive destruction. It shows that loose structures of yellow iron hydroxide had been formed which at first partially adhered to the surface, and finally became detached, leaving the surface of the metal bare and open to further attacks. The picture also gives an indication that rust formed in this way has a much greater volume than the metal from which it originates, so that, if formed under a protective coating, it either will break through the coating, making it porous, or will detach the protective layer entirely from its base.

The destructive action of oxidation and hydrolysis is greatly aggravated by mechanical forces which develop while the film is drying, and grow in strength while the dried film is ageing. The life of a surface coating film is dominated by a continuous battle of internal tensions against the elastic forces of the film, caused by pull, pressure, expansion, con-

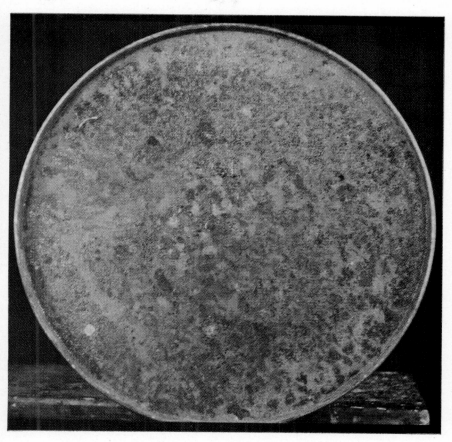

FIGURE 20. Destructive corrosion on iron.

traction, bending, flexing and other factors. The attacks usually start at weak spots in the surface coating, such as small pores, scratches, foreign matter, air inclusions or at points weakened by chemical action.

Figure 21 gives an

idea of the internal stresses

acting in resin containing surface coating layers. They are made visible by photographing a transparent film under the microscope with polarized light, under which the fields of internal stresses light up, whereas the areas, in which no

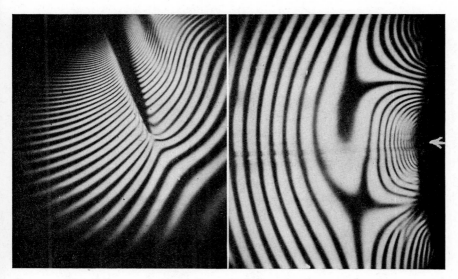

FIGURE 21. Micro photographs of internal stresses in transparent surface coatings.

elastic tensions have developed, remain dark. The picture on the left hand side shows the elastic tensions in a film that has been pulled apart until rupture occurs. The break is apparent from the deep vertical crack surrounded by very pronounced tension fields. The right hand picture demonstrates tension fields developed when a needle, indicated in the photograph by an arrow, is pressed against the film.

Another example of making visible to the eye stress conditions in surface coatings, is given in *Figure 22*, representing sections of four different types of surface wrinkles. These

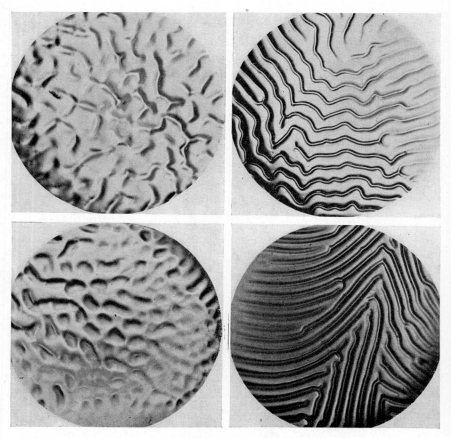

FIGURE 22.   Mechanical tensions in wrinkles of surface coatings.

photographic close-ups, taken with ordinary light, while the object is illuminated laterally, show spectacular surface irregularities, which are formed by the action of strong mechanical forces.

The laboratory technique for

the taking of microphotographs

is of interest to all research workers. The main optical apparatus used is a photomicrographic camera, its microscope having all modern accessories. Illumination is provided, either by a white electrical bulb of sufficient strength, or by a yellow neon tube. Both ordinary and polarized light are used for the photographic exposure.

Ordinary light is made use of in different ways, depending upon the particular photographic effect desired. Transmitted light is used for illumination from below, incident light for obtaining perpendicular views from above. Dark field, lateral and vertical illumination have their special places. Lateral illumination proves most effective when the two planes of the object and of the rays approach the parallel. Then even the smallest inequalities of the surface give shadows and become visible.

When applying polarized light, the object is placed between a polarizer and an analyzer. The linearly polarized light obtained in this way is often unsuitable for microphotographic purposes, because large parts of the visual field are blacked out. To avoid this partial darkening, circularly polarized light must be used. It is obtained by inserting two optically active plates of a quarter of a wave length between analyzer and polarizer, the proper azimuth being determined empirically.

When a yellow neon tube is used as the light source for producing polarized rays, black and white pictures are obtained in which the isotropic parts are dark and the doubly refracting areas are light. When, instead of the monochromatic yellow sodium light, a lamp is used which supplies intense white light, all colors of the spectrum appear, which can be photographed on color sensitive films.

The proper time of exposure for microphotographic pictures must be determined empirically; the correct amount of light is more important for colored films than for black and white films. In making colored pictures, a slight under-exposure blackens the field, and a slight over-exposure does not produce color effects at all.

Considering stress and strain conditions in layers of oxidized oils, straight oil films usually are found to be too plastic or too elastic to allow the development of internal tensile tensions.

Stress conditions,

however, are created when hard resins are combined with the oil, growing with the amount of resin added, and varying with the type of resin used. The influence of resins on mechanical film properties can be evaluated scientifically by measuring, under controlled conditions, the film distensibility and tensile strength of well defined resin-oil combinations. But it is practically impossible to take into proper consideration a number of factors, which largely influence the two characteristics of tensile strength and distensibility as, for instance, the amount of solvent which remains in the dried film, the type and surface condition of the support to which the film is attached, the type and degree of film adhesion and other causes.

Attempts have been made to evaluate physical film properties by accurately measuring the abrasion resistance for which various methods are available. In this type of resin evaluation, a rubbing apparatus is useful, which is similar in principle to a windshield wiper, with a device to count the number of strokes necessary to rub down a film of given thickness.

For practical purposes, it is entirely satisfactory to evaluate the resin influence on mechanical film properties by the simple method of determining

the Kauri reduction value.

The Kauri value is not related to any particular physical or mechanical film property, but measures a variety of properties, including both adhesion and toughness, and also furnishes a reliable picture of the performance to be expected from the dried film when applied and exposed under practical conditions. As a rule, the Kauri value is a more reliable indication of durability and weather resistance than the accelerated weathering test.

The official Kauri reduction test is described in detail in many specifications. It measures the amount of hard Kauri gum necessary to lower the elasticity of the dried surface coating, determined by a bending test, to a certain specified degree. Therefore, high Kauri values indicate high elasticity and toughness. Kauri values, on the other hand, do not measure the elasticity of the resins themselves; for instance, very brittle resins, like pure phenolics, may have high values, whereas resins like modified phenolics which, as such, show definite elastic properties of their own, may have comparatively low Kauri values.

Kauri reduction measurements, carried out on 25 gallon linseed oil varnishes on the base of the various resins considered in this study, showed high Kauri values of about 100 for pure phenol resins, and only about half of this amount for modified phenolics, maleics and copal-type synthetics. The values varied among and within the latter three groups with the drying time, quick drying resins yielding lower Kauri values than the slow drying types. If the varnishes were adjusted to equal drying times, the figures obtained indicated a favorable influence of the oil reactivity of the resins on their Kauri value. The extremely high Kauri figures of pure phenolics demonstrate their superiority in the production of elastic and weather resistant finishes.

The film resistance obtained by the use of today's resins is excellent. However, further improvements may be expected and

resins with new and unusual combinations

of property characteristics will be created. One of the important forward steps will be elimination of the old established interrelationship between certain resin constants, for instance, the rule that high melting points are linked with high viscosities, and that high viscosities are firmly connected with low solubilities. The result of this work is, that high melting point resins will be developed, which will be distinguished by low viscosities and high solubilities.

Other steps forward in resin production will be the improvement of bodying and drying characteristics, and a further advance in the oil reactivity of resins. This development in turn will broaden the field of practically useful oils, especially among the semi-oxidizing types; will lead to more freedom in the formulation of coatings; and will allow the production of more versatile finishes.

Chapter VII

Influence of Resins on Printing Inks

It has been pointed out that the methods of identification, evaluation and application of coating resins differ in many ways from those used for ink resins. The difference appears clearly from the following comments on the influence of resins on printing inks, covering the physical characteristics of ink resins and the performance of resin-oil combinations in inks.

PHYSICAL CHARACTERISTICS OF INK RESINS

The physical characteristic of melting point is an essential factor in judging the usefulness of ink resins, especially for overprint varnishes and gloss inks, and it can be stated that, as a rule, a minimum melting point of 145° to 150° C is required to develop sufficient printability and gloss, and to prevent penetration. The maximum obtainable

melting point of ink resins

amounts to about 175° to 180° C. If this limit is exceeded, the resins become insoluble in vegetable and mineral oils.

The preferred methods for melting point determinations of printing ink resins are the same as those used for coating resins. In addition, the sliding-bar method is in use, in which the resin powder is sprinkled on an electrically heated wire coil, the temperature of which increases from one end to the other. A distinct line of demarkation develops between the molten and the solid material at a definite temperature, which is determined by a thermocouple in conjunction with a potentiometer.

The high melting point of ink resins is necessary to counteract the softening action of volatile solvents, especially kerosene, which are very firmly retained in the resins. Unless evaporated by heat, as in heat set inks, the resins retain solvents to the extent of more than 10% of the resin weight, and such residual solvents may lower the melting points by 25° to 50° C. Peculiarly enough, the softening influence of residual solvents is of the same order of magnitude for all resins under discussion. The fusibility of the ink resins is of the same character as that of coating resins, and is subject to the same relationship between fluidity and temperature, which is discussed in detail in the previous chapter.

The melting point of the ink resins, discussed in this study, is directly proportional to their viscosity. Resins with melting points of about 150° C. have a viscosity of about 20 poises in 60% xylol solution. Both melting points and viscosities increase in direct proportion, reaching the practically obtainable upper limit of melting points at 175° C.-180° C. and of corresponding viscosities at about 150 poises. As a rule, resins with viscosities higher than 150 poises cannot be manufactured in normal equipment, because they become gelatinous and infusible. Resins with viscosities lower than 15 poises are usually unsuitable for printing inks, because they cause too much tack and penetration of the ink.

The viscosity of ink resins can be determined in the same way as that of coating resins, *i.e.* either in the molten state or in solution. The first

method of viscosity determination

is often used in resin production by measuring the power input necessary to turn the agitator in the fused resin. The second method is in common use for routine laboratory testing.

The viscosity of ink resins in solution can be determined in two different ways, *i.e.* either by dissolving the resins in a volatile solvent or in linseed oil heated to 150° to 300° C. The method of dissolving the resins in volatile solvents follows the procedure used for coating resins, *i.e.* 60% xylol solutions are prepared and their viscosity is recorded according to the Gardner scale. If the resins are free of gelatinous matter and completely soluble in xylol, the results obtained are indicative of the practical performance of the resins in ink manufacture. If, however, overpolymerized parts are present, which are insoluble in xylol, the viscosity values in Gardner terms do not furnish a true picture of resin performance, because the gelatinous matter has no opportunity to show its influence.

Inasmuch as gelatinous particles are often present, it is generally preferred to dissolve the resins completely in linseed oil at the lowest temperature possible, and to record the viscosities of a linseed oil solution, which contains 33% resin, in time values determined by viscometers of the Stormer type. In this way, the overpolymerized parts show their true importance.

Some resins contain gelatinous matter which is insoluble, not only in solvents, but also in heated oils. Such resins should not be evaluated in terms of viscosity, because their merits are shown by other factors, such as production of gloss or reduction of penetration.

Viscosity determination of ink resins in oil solution is usually carried out as follows. One part of resin and two parts of a low viscous litho oil are heated together with a temperature increase of 5° C. per minute. Samples are taken at regular intervals and the heating is interrupted when the sample stays brilliantly clear after being cooled to room temperature. The maximum temperature necessary to reach this point is noted as the clearing point. It may vary within the limits of 150° and 300° C. The viscosity of the clear resin-oil combination is measured in a viscometer, preferably a Stormer instrument, adjusted to a temperature of 25° C. and a pulling weight of 750 gram. Viscosity values are either given as time values in minutes or as absolute figures in poises. Measured in time units, the Stormer viscosity of ink resins in oil solution varies within wide limits, *i.e.* within the range of a few minutes to more than one hour.

An interesting relationship exists between Gardner and Stormer viscosity values. Typical readings are recorded in *Table 17* for four different resins, *i.e.* a copal-type synthetic, a modified phenolic, and two high viscosity types of maleic resins. One of the maleics is completely soluble both in xylol and heated oil, while the other one is partially gelled and contains overpolymerized particles, not soluble in xylol but soluble in oil heated to 260° C.

Table 17. Relationship of Gardner and Stormer Viscosity Readings

Resin Types	*Gardner Reading*	*Stormer Reading*	*Ratio of Gardner to Stormer Readings*
Copal-type synthetic	$V = 9$ poises	6 minutes	1.50 : 1
Modified phenolic	$Y = 18$ poises	12 minutes	1.50 : 1
Modified maleic	$Z_3 = 45$ poises	30 minutes	1.50 : 1
Modified maleic, partially gelled	$Z_4 = 63$ poises	50 minutes	1.25 : 1

Table 17 shows the perfect proportionality of Gardner and Stormer readings for the first three resin types, all of which contained no gelatinous particles, whereas the fourth resin deviated considerably from this proportionality, the Stormer viscosity being substantially higher than that of the Gardner reading, *i.e.* 50 minutes instead of 42 minutes. This increase was due to the fact that highly viscous resin particles went into solution in the hot oil, but not in the boiling xylol.

As appears from the foregoing comments

the degree of solubility

of printing ink resins in solvents and oils is of great importance in their practical evaluation. Resin solubilty governs the performance of resins with volatile solvents as used for heat set inks, rotogravure inks, steam set inks, and also governs the combination of resins with oils, forming the base for the majority of ink vehicles.

Most printing ink resins under consideration are soluble in strong solvents, such as aromatic hydrocarbons and organic ester solvents. The solutions can be diluted to low solid contents without precipitation of the resin. The solubility is limited in aliphatic hydrocarbons, such as high boiling cuts of mineral oil, especially kerosene, the degree of solubility decreasing with the Kauri-butanol value of the solvent. Whereas, it is possible to produce ink resins perfectly soluble in kerosene, of a Kauri-butanol value of 32, it is hardly feasible to make resins, which are satisfactorily soluble in mineral oils, with Kauri-butanol values lower than 22.

The degree of resin solubility in mineral oils can be determined by the titration method, described in detail for coating resins. Another method is based on the fact that resin solubility is inversely proportional to the

minimum concentration of the kerosene solution

which will stay clear and will not precipitate resinous or crystalline matter on standing at room temperature. The minimum concentration can be correctly established by preparing solutions with varying solid contents and observing their stability. In a series of tests with kerosene, of a Kauri-butanol value of 34, the minimum concentrations were found to be widely different, *i.e.* 80% for a low solubility maleic, 50% for a rosin-modified bis phenol resin, 25% for an alkyl phenol resin and 10% for a copal-type synthetic. These figures indicate that alkyl phenol resins possess better solubility than bis phenol resins and that copal-type resins are of better solubility than both phenolics and maleics.

The solubility of ink resins in alcohol, which is an important property for certain inks as, for instance, aniline inks, can be determined by titrating the 60% resin solution in xylol with waterfree alcohol until an incipient turbidity appears. The majority of ink resins have only a negligibly small alcohol tolerance. Non-esterified, rosin-modified phenolics possess a substantial tolerance, and certain highly acid maleics and fumarics have a very high tolerance for alcohol.

Ink resins of the non-esterified rosin maleic or fumaric type are soluble in diethylene glycol and other polyglycols, and form the base for steam set inks. Their solutions are distinguished by a peculiarly high tolerance for water, not observed in any other ink resins. Water tolerance can be determined in the customary way by titration with water or by preparing glycol solutions in which the water content is gradually increased. It is found that as much as 25 to 30% of water is tolerated.

When the solutions of ink resins in volatile solvents are spread out in thin layers, the major part of the solvent evaporates, but a noticeable amount of

solvent is retained by the resin.

The degree of solvent retention does not depend on the type of the resin, but is greatly influenced by the thickness of the layer, the volatility of the solvent and by the temperature of drying. The thickness of ink layers is usually smaller than that of surface coatings, and accordingly the amount of retained solvents is generally smaller in inks than in coatings, where it amounts to substantial percentages—more than 10%. On the other hand, the volatility of ink solvents is often lower than that of solvents used for coatings, favoring solvent retention in printing inks.

Retained solvents have the disadvantage of softening the resinous ink layer, but exert some beneficial effect by making the resin component more compatible with added substances, such as soaps, greases and waxes.

The solubility of ink resins in drying oils is determined by establishing the minimum temperature at which clear resin-oil combinations are obtained under standardized conditions, as described in detail for coating resins. Whereas there are no serious objections to high clearing temperatures for coating resins, printing ink resins are required to possess low points of clarification, in order to avoid penetration, which is undesirable in glossy ink materials. As a rule, only resins that dissolve clearly in oil at temperatures lower than 260° C. or 500° F. are suitable for ink purposes. Normally resins of such low clearing points do not have the high melting points and viscosities required for printing ink purposes. To obtain such property combinations, ink resins, therefore, have to be especially adjusted in their chemical composition and method of processing.

RESIN-OIL COMBINATIONS IN INKS

Chemical and physical resin properties which have been previously discussed are transferred in various ways into the resin combination with drying oils, in which form the bulk of ink resins is consumed. The resin characteristics exert a manifold influence on the manner in which printing inks are produced and used. They influence the stability of the inks on storage, their printability, speed of drying and degree of penetration. They control the gloss of overprint varnishes and gloss inks, the bronzing properties, the hardness and rubproofness, and the water and alkali resistance of the printed inks.

Practical ink making prepares ink vehicles containing resins by fusing resin and oil gently together, adjusting time and temperature so that no oil bodying and no resin oil reaction takes place. This results in a physically homogeneous solution which does not separate on cooling. Quite different from the procedure used for making surface coating varnishes, the process of producing resin-containing printing ink vehicles strictly avoids a co-polymerization of resin and oil because such co-polymerization leads to penetration and loss of gloss.

Therefore, the interesting relationships among the resin characteristics of bodying speed and the resin oil reactivity, described in the previous chapter on coating resins, have no bearing on ink vehicles.

The process of dissolving the resins in oils is governed by the solubility of the resins in the oils, which is measured by the temperature of clarification according to previously described methods. The most suitable clearing point depends largely on the purpose for which the ink is being prepared, but as a rule should not exceed 500° F.

The viscosity of resin-oil combinations to be converted into ink vehicles is the arithmetical mean of the individual viscosities of the two components, provided no gelatinous matter is present. Inasmuch as oil-soluble resins free of gelatinous particles and of extremely high viscosity are available, very viscous ink vehicles can be prepared without resorting to special cooking procedures.

Under certain circumstances, resin-oil ink vehicles show

a tendency to after-body

i.e. to gain viscosity on storage without outside influences. The after-bodying of clear ink liquids is accelerated by the presence of drier metals and is stimulated by high viscosity oils, and also is largely influenced by the characteristics of the resinous component. The tendency to after-body decreases with the acidity of the resin and with the degree of resin solubility. On the other hand, this tendency increases with the relative amount of overpolymerized gelatinous material present in the resin.

After-bodying of the unpigmented vehicles is directly related to their tendency to liver with reactive pigments. Therefore, all factors, particularly those controlled by the resin characteristics which increase after-bodying will promote livering. Only the resin acidity forms an exception to this rule, because it increases livering but reduces after-bodying. This factor, however, is not of importance because the reactivity of resinous acids with sensitive pigments, like zinc oxide or peacock blue, is much less pronounced than that of fatty acids present in resin oil vehicles and, therefore, in ink vehicles is entirely overshadowed by the activities of fatty acids.

The most important factor governing pigment stability is the presence of high molecular resinous particles, which are induced to gelatinization by the surface action of reactive pigments. Therefore, resins which are of a molecularly homogeneous structure and which do not contain overpolymerized portions, such as highly matured phenol resins or copal-type synthetic resins, are best suited to the production of non-livering inks.

The customary accelerated method of testing pigment stability consists in placing a well ground paste of equal parts of peacock blue and vehicle in an electric oven, which is maintained at a constant temperature of 80° C. A paste, which will not liver under these conditions within 80 hours, can be considered stable for a period of several months under normal conditions.

Most printing ink resins are applied for the particular purpose of producing inks, or overprint varnishes which will result in quick drying, hard, resistant and glossy prints. The part played by the resins in the production of such prints affects the step of printing the ink or the overprint varnish, the process of drying of the wet layer, and is largely responsible for the appearance and the performance of the final print.

When printing inks or overprint varnishes, based on resin-containing vehicles, are spread out in thin layers in the printing process, their

printability depends on manifold factors

among which the characteristics of the resin present are of paramount importance. Printability of inks is sometimes determined by the elaborate inkometer. For the purpose of resin evaluation, printability can be measured in a simpler but sufficiently accurate way, by determining the degree of tackiness of the ink.

To demonstrate the interesting relationship of resin characteristics and printability, resin-oil combinations of five different resins, all varying in viscosity and chemical composition, were prepared and their tackiness determined. The resins used were a copal-type synthetic, a medium viscosity maleic, a medium viscosity phenolic, a high viscosity phenolic and a high viscosity maleic. They were combined with certain litho-oils by heating a sample to the point that it stayed clear on cooling. To exclude the influence of other substances, no additions of solvents, waxes or driers were made. To eliminate the influence of the viscosity, which increases the tack of vehicles of the same composition in direct proportion, all resin-oil combinations were adjusted to the same viscosity, *i.e.* to a running time on the Stormer viscometer of 13 minutes at 25° C. with a 750-gram pulling weight.

The equalization of the two viscosities was carried out in two different series. In one series the ratio of resin to oil was kept constant at one to two, while the viscosity of the oil was varied from *A* to *T*. In the other series the viscosity of the litho oil was kept constant at *G*, while the ratio of resin to oil was changed from 100 to 150 up to 100 to 230. All viscosity figures were given in Gardner values. In the case of the resins the reference is to the 60% solution in xylol; in the case of the oils the reference is to the straight oils themselves.

As a measure of the printability of the resin-oil combinations previously described

the degree of tack

was determined by pulling a strip of uncoated cellophane from a surface printed with these combinations, in a simple device built for this purpose. A given weight of the resin-oil mixture was rolled in a thin layer over a given surface space of a glass

or metal plate, on to which a strip of cellophane eight inches
long and one inch wide was closely pressed, eliminating all
air bubbles. One end of the strip was then pulled by a thin
thread running over a small pulley, carrying a given weight.
The time, determined by a stop watch in seconds, necessary
to pull up the strip was recorded as a measure of the degree of
tackiness. It varied under the conditions chosen for these
experiments from 15 seconds, for non-tacky substances, to 45
seconds for highly tacky materials.

Table 18 records the results obtained with each of the two
series carried out with the five resins. The time figures, in
seconds, are the average of a large number of determinations
and, therefore, are reliable values. Their accuracy is further

Table 18. Influence of Resins on Printability

Type of Resin	Resin Viscosity	Same Resin to Oil Ratio		Varying Resin to Oil Ratio	
		Oil Viscosity	Tack in Seconds	Parts of Oil on 100 Parts Resin	Tack in Seconds
Copal-type synthetic	N	T	30	150	30
Medium viscosity maleic	P	R	29	160	29
Medium viscosity phenolic	Z	G	26	200	26
High viscosity phenolic	Z_3	C	21	220	21
High viscosity maleic	Z_4	A	20	230	20

confirmed by the fact that they were found to be identical in
both series of tests, *i.e.* in both the tests in which the resin to
oil ratio remained identical and also the tests in which the
resin to oil ratio was varied.

The comparison of the tack values, found for the copal-type
synthetic, the medium viscosity phenolic and the high viscosity

maleic, proves that the tack is inversely proportional to the resin viscosity, *i.e.* high viscosity resins yield non-tacky vehicles, while low viscosity resins yield highly tacky vehicles. This finding is in accordance with the experience from daily practice, that low viscosity resins often give inks that pull the paper; it is also in accordance with the practical rule that, in order to produce workable inks, it is necessary to lower either the viscosity of the oil or to reduce, as far as practically possible, the relative amount of the oil.

The comparison of the copal-type synthetic to the maleic of about the same viscosity shows the same tackiness for both resins; or, comparing the two high viscosity type phenolic and maleic resins, it is found that both resins have the same tackiness. These observations prove conclusively that the chemical nature of the resins has no influence on the amount of tack produced by them in the ink vehicles.

Considered from the resin angle in the

drying of the printed ink or overprint varnish

the porosity of the printed surface is of importance. On non-porous surfaces, the drying process is due to the evaporation of the solvent, followed by the oxidation and polymerization of the remaining layer in a manner very similar to the drying of surface coatings. Accordingly, the resin influence in this case is similar to that explained in detail under coating resins.

However, on porous surfaces such as paper, which represents by far the largest part of printing, penetration is a decided factor. In paper printing, drying by oxidation and polymerization is only of secondary importance, and the formation of a dry layer is mainly due to the penetration of the vehicle into the paper base. Offsetting and sticking of stacked sheets depends chiefly on the amount of material remaining on the paper surface, *i.e.* on the thickness of the printing and the degree of penetration.

Penetration is due not only to the ability of the ink material to vertically sink into the paper, but also to spread out horizontally and laterally. Paper printing offers abundant opportunities for this type of vertical and horizontal spreading, because the printing procedure seldom produces a continuous surface layer of ink and, in most cases, distributes the ink in a network of isolated ink spots.

A good example of these conditions is shown in *Figure 23*. The picture shows a microscopic photograph, magnified one hundred times, of a red ink, printed as solid dark red on the

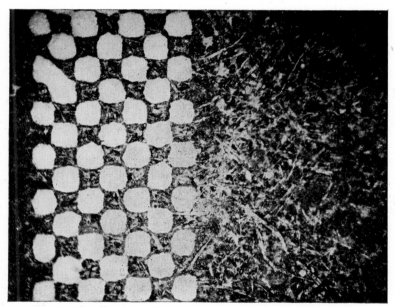

FIGURE 23. Microscopic view of an ink printed on paper.

right hand side, and as a lighter colored red screen on the left. In order to make the minutest structural details of the printed surface clearly visible, a special type of microscopic lighting was used in this picture, *i.e.* the dark field, vertical illumination, based on conically incident light, arranged in a way that only a minimum of reflected light entered the visual field. The photograph shows that even the solid portion of the print, supposedly completely covered by ink, does not have a fully homogeneous surface, because of the fibrous structure of the paper. The light colored portion, incompletely covered by ink, is dotted with unprinted areas, which interrupt the coherent surface and lay it wide open to penetration.

The influence of ink resins on

drying by penetration

is directly related to the way in which resins change the penetrating capabilities of oils. If resins and oils are combined through the use of a strong, mutual solvent, without applying heat, penetration is pronounced. If resins and oils are combined through heating the mixture to the point where it is clear and homogeneous only while hot, such a vehicle separates, becomes cloudy on cooling and may print with strong penetration. By increasing the degree of dispersion or solution of the resin in the oil, the penetration is reduced. The minimum of penetrating properities is reached when resin and oil are heated to the point at which the combination stays clear on cooling. On continued heating the tendency of the resin-oil combination to penetrate increases rapidly again.

Normal inks, on the base of straight oil vehicles, dry to give prints which have little or no gloss. The incorporation of resins into the oil produces ink materials, both of the clear, unpigmented and of the pigmented type which, on drying, yield glossy prints. The three resin classes of rosin-modified phenolics, modified maleics and copal-type synthetics, discussed in this book, have great merits for the production of such ink materials, *i.e.* of both overprint varnishes and gloss inks. Their

effect on gloss production

has been made the object of a special experimental study, which is described in the following paragraphs.

For this purpose a Vandercook proving press was used. This press proved very accurate in ink distribution and permitted

FIGURE 24. Vandercook proving press during operation.

reliable comparisons of the various ink materials. To make sure that identical amounts of ink materials were applied per square inch of printed surface, equal quantities were weighed out and transferred to the rollers.

The press used for this study is pictured in the colored *Figure 24,* which shows the machine when it is ready for the printing of test sheets. A measured amount of red gloss ink had just been applied to the inking equipment, consisting of various rollers, and had been spread out uniformly over the large center steel roller, which serves as distributor of the ink. As the step following the one shown in the photograph, the printing plate is inked by moving the rollers over its surface in the usual manner, leaving a uniform ink layer on top of the printing plate. The sheet visible on the table of the press is a double coated litho paper, held in place by the gripping mechanism and ready to be carried by the impression cylinder to the plate. A mechanical time controller is used to properly time the comparative tests.

Printing was done in all cases on white coated paper and the prints were allowed to dry at room temperature, fully exposed to light and air. Part of the overprint varnishes was also printed on paper, which had been preprinted with a colored non-gloss ink for the purpose of eliminating the penetration of the varnish into the paper. After drying, the gloss of the prints was measured by a standard glossmeter or, in case of conspicuous differences, the gloss was compared visually and graded.

In preparing overprint varnishes for the comparative tests, it had to be considered that factors, other than those connected with resins, have a bearing on

gloss conditions in overprint varnishes.

For instance, gloss is influenced by additions of waxes, greases, and drier pastes, all of which tend to reduce the gloss. Gloss, furthermore, depends on the type of kerosene or paraffin oil used. The higher the boiling range of the mineral oil, the more the overprint varnish, of which it is a part, tends to penetrate into the paper and thereby loses its gloss.

Gloss also depends on the viscosity and the type of oil used. It grows with the degree of viscosity, becoming very pronounced with oil viscosities higher than Z, if the varnish is applied on preprinted paper. However, on bare paper, which allows penetration, the influence of increased viscosity is small, because it is counteracted by the gloss reducing effect of penetration which also grows with the viscosity. However, the chemical nature of the litho oils used has a decided influence on gloss. For instance, oils polymerized under vacuum or carbon dioxide produce much less gloss than oils bodied in open kettles, even when the acid values of both oils are the same.

The influence of all these factors was carefully eliminated in determining the role played by ink resins in overprint varnishes, and also care was taken that the varnishes being compared were of practically the same viscosity. In several series of systematic tests, great numbers of overprint varnishes were investigated, varying the method of incorporating the resin into the oil, the ratio of resin to oil, changing the acid values, and also the viscosities and the composition of the resins. The results reported in the following paragraphs demonstrate many interesting relationships which, at the same time, give practical hints as to the ways and means of regulating the gloss of ink materials by the proper use of resins.

The method of

combining resin and oil

influences gloss, particularly in the case of resins which are difficult to dissolve, *i.e.* resins which do not form a complete oil solution when heated with the oil slightly above the melting point of the resins.

Resins of low solubility give flat prints when the ink vehicle is prepared by dispersing the resin in the oil at room temperature through grinding on a roller mill or through the use of a strong common solvent. They yield a print of medium gloss when the resin is heated with the oil to a temperature at which the batch is clear, while hot, but clouds again when cold. The gloss of the dried overprint varnish increases on further heating of the resin-oil mixture contained in the varnish and reaches a maximum at the point when the resin and oil are sufficiently combined to give a clear sample when cooled. The gloss of the prints decreases again on further cooking of the resin oil mixture forming the base of the ink vehicle, because more volatile solvent is required in the ink to compensate for the viscosity increase of the resin-oil combination, and also because the latter develops, with continued heating, a decided tendency to penetration.

These observations refute the general opinion that resins, when merely dissolved in oil, yield better gloss than when completely combined through heat, and disproves the conception that a simple colloidal resin oil solution, when spread out on paper, separates into its components. According to this theory, the oil part penetrates into the paper with the effect of good adhesion and drying, whereas the resin part remains as a coherent layer on top of the paper, producing high gloss. The previously described observations, however, confirm the conclusion that through the co-polymerization of resin and oil at the proper temperature a homogeneous compound is formed which does not separate and penetrates uniformly into the paper.

The influence of the

resin to oil ratio

was investigated by varying the amount of oil in varnishes based on phenolics, maleics and copal-type synthetics, using in the varnish about 15% of kerosene and the customary additions of lead acetate, wax and drier paste. Resins and oils were heated only to the point that the mixture stayed clear on cooling, and any further heating was carefully avoided. The printing of the varnishes showed that the gloss on preprinted paper surfaces was higher with increased relative amounts of oil, and proved that the gloss on bare paper increased only until a resin-to-oil ratio of one to one-and-a-half is reached. Larger relative amounts of oil do not further improve the gloss on plain paper, because penetration becomes too pronounced.

Evaluating, in a similar manner, the significance of resin acidity in gloss development of ink materials containing such resins, it was found that gloss is not appreciably affected by slight changes in the acid values of the resins. Acid values higher than 40 seem to reduce the gloss; very high acid values of more than 100, characteristic of non-esterfied modified phenolics, cause practically complete flatness of the overprint.

Varying the resin viscosity in the test series, printing results were obtained which proved clearly that the

viscosity of the resin is the predominant factor

in the relationship of gloss and resin properties and, more specifically, it was found that there exists a critical degree of viscosity for each resin group. If the viscosity increased beyond this degree, the gloss decreased; if it decreased below this critical value, the gloss also decreased. A practical lower limit was reached when the ink viscosity was reduced to a point where the product became too tacky for use in printing.

The following general rules were found to apply to the three groups of phenolics, maleics and copal-type synthetics. Rosin-modified phenol resins had an optimum viscosity of Z, determined in 60% xylol solution on the Gardner scale, with a lower limit of about V. The optimum viscosity of maleic resins was slightly higher with a viscosity of Z, the lower limit again being V. As a rule, maleics required more kerosene than phenolics to attain the same viscosity, the larger amount of kerosene counteracting the gloss. The optimum viscosity of copal-type synthetics was lower than that of both phenolics or maleics.

Finally, investigating the gloss-producing effect of the various chemical compositions of the resins, it was established that gloss was not substantially affected by chemical composition. As a rule, the highest gloss was obtained by phenolic resins, followed closely by the other two resin classes, provided their viscosity was high enough to fall within the optimal range. The surface appearance obtained by copal-type synthetics, as compared to that produced with phenolics, was distinguished more by smoothness than by specular gloss. Combinations of both resin types yielded prints which were outstanding in both specular gloss and smoothness of the print.

The previous comments have shown how the gloss of overprint varnishes can be regulated by the use of the ink resins discussed in this book. Similar rules govern the production of

high-gloss, colored printing inks

as evidenced by two series of gloss inks, in which the chemical nature and the viscosity of the resinous component was systematically varied. The gloss inks were printed by means of the previously described proof press on white coated paper and after complete drying, *i.e.* usually after 24 hours, their gloss was determined by visual comparison. The differences in gloss were mostly so pronounced that no glossmeter readings were required.

To obtain comparable results in this series of tests, it had to be considered that gloss depends upon a number of factors, other than the nature of the resins, which had to be taken into account. Gloss depends upon pigment content varying, as a rule, from high gloss at 10 to 20% to low gloss at 20 to 30%, all figures being relative and largely dependent upon the oil-absorption value of the pigment. The experimental comparisons were carried out with the same pigment in all cases, amounting to about 16%, which brought out clearly the existing differences in gloss.

Gloss is also governed by the viscosity of the oil incorporated into the vehicle, increasing with the degree of viscosity, a factor which was eliminated as far as possible. Furthermore, gloss depends on the ratio of resin to oil in the ink vehicle and on the viscosity of the ink itself. Both factors were equalized by using, for the gloss comparison, ink vehicles with identical ratios of 8 parts of resin to 14 parts of oil, and by adjusting all inks tested to the same viscosity of 20 minutes running time on the Stormer instrument at 25° C. under a weight of 750 grams.

The ink vehicles were prepared by heating resin and oil slowly to the temperature at which they were combined sufficiently to yield a clear pill when cold. Upon cooling, 2% of a 4% cobalt paste was added. No mineral oil was used. 80 parts of this ink vehicle were then mixed with 40 parts of a red pigment paste, prepared by grinding equal parts of a red lake toner and a litho oil of about one poise viscosity until perfect smoothness in texture was obtained.

To establish the influence of the chemical composition of various

resin types on the degree of gloss

of inks of the glossy type, the main representatives of the three resin classes of phenolics, maleics, and copal-type synthetics were compared, care being taken that ink viscosity,

Table 19. Influence of Resin Composition on Gloss of Gloss Inks

Type of Resins	Resin Viscosity	Oil Viscosity	Gloss Appearance of Print
Modified bis phenol resin	W	G	high gloss
Modified maleic resin	T	G	medium gloss
Copal-type synthetic resin	V	G	medium gloss

resin-to-oil ratio, pigment content and, more particularly, the viscosity of the oil and of the resins used, were kept practically identical. The results are reported in *Table 19*.

The survey shows an influence of the chemical nature of the resins to the effect that phenolic resins yield higher gloss in gloss inks than either maleics or copal-type synthetics, all other conditions being equal.

To determine the role played by

resin viscosity in gloss production

three series of tests were carried out using a phenolic, a maleic and a copal-type synthetic, varying for each resin only its viscosity, keeping all other conditions as identical as possible. The results obtained with a modified maleic resin are reported in *Table 20*.

Table 20. Influence of Resin Viscosity on Gloss of Gloss Inks

Resin Used	*Viscosity of Resin*	*Viscosity of Oil*	*Gloss Appearance of Print*
High viscosity maleic	Z_2	G	high gloss
Medium viscosity maleic	U	K	medium gloss
Low viscosity maleic	F	V	no gloss

Corresponding findings were made with the two other resin types. From the results obtained it may be concluded that gloss is directly proportional to the viscosity of the resins. The gloss increases with the resin viscosity, in spite of the fact that the oil viscosity had to be decreased to keep the body of the ink on the same viscosity level. Further tests also showed that the lack of gloss, due to low viscosity resins, is so pronounced that it cannot be compensated for by the use of high viscosity oils.

Resin viscosity clearly governs the gloss of printing inks, which are based on resin-containing vehicles. In a similar way resin viscosity influences the peculiar

phenomenon of bronzing

which is observed in certain pigmented printing inks. This interesting relationship was brought out by the following experiment.

Four gloss ink vehicles were prepared by heating 16 parts of the different type resins with 28 parts of various litho oils until clear cold pills were obtained. Upon cooling, one part of a 4% cobalt paste was added. The resins used were a copal-type synthetic and a modified maleic, both in low and high viscosity types. The litho oils used were varied in viscosity so as to yield the same Stormer consistency of the finished pigmented ink. To achieve this result, only relatively small variations of the oil viscosities, *i.e.* changes within the range of 2-8 poises, were required. To introduce the pigment, a colored paste was prepared by thoroughly grinding equal parts of a red lake toner with a thin litho oil and one part of this red paste was mixed with two parts of the vehicle previously described.

The resulting ink was printed on white coated paper by means of the proving press and the appearance of the dried prints observed. *Table 21* gives the results obtained. In

Table 21. Influence of Resin Viscosity on Bronzing of Color Inks

Type of Resin Used	*Viscosity of Resin by Gardner Scale*	*Viscosity of Oil in Ink*	*Viscosity of Ink on Stormer Viscometer*	*Appearance of Print*
Low viscosity copal-type synthetic	K	6 poises	19 minutes	strongly bronzing
High viscosity copal-type synthetic	V	3 poises	20 minutes	no bronzing
Low viscosity modified maleic	F	8 poises	20 minutes	strongly bronzing
High viscosity modified maleic	Z_2	2 poises	21 minutes	no bronzing

both cases, the low viscosity resins yielded strongly bronzing prints, whereas the high viscosity resins produced inks with no bronzing effects in the prints, proving conclusively that bronzing depends on resin viscosity.

The mechanical and chemical resistance of prints obtained from orthodox oil-based inks is of a much lower order of magnitude than that of protective surface coatings. As a rule, this comparatively low resistance level of the prints is sufficient for practical purposes. There are, however, applications where a higher degree of mechanical strength and chemical stability is required. This effect is achieved by the incorporation of resins into the ink vehicles.

Resins improve the

mechanical properties

of scratch resistance and rubproofness of prints. These characteristics improve with the amount of resin incorporated into the film-forming material, and their values increase with the melting point and the oil reactivity of the resin used. The mechanical improvement of the prints is particularly pronounced, if resins are incorporated which possess a strong accelerating effect on oxidation drying, such as bis phenol resins or copal-type synthetics. It has been suggested to measure rubproofness accurately, and to record it in figures, by a device which consists of a vacuum-operated windshield wiper, having a speed control and an automatic counter to record the number of strokes necessary to rub off the layer.

Resins furthermore improve

the chemical stability of the prints

by reinforcing the vehicle against the attacks of water, alkali and other chemicals. This reinforcing effect depends on the same factors discussed in detail for coating resins and is particularly noticeable in the case of modified phenol resins. The

waterproofing effect of the resins is desirable for many purposes, as for instance for soap resisting inks, and has shown
merits for lithographic ink vehicles which are exposed to the
saponifying and emulsifying action of the dampening solution.

The improvement of ink properties through the incorporation of resins of the type under discussion is well established.
But the development work will not stop here and new resins,
with novel and unique property combinations, are in sight.
Interesting examples of the new trends are the high viscosity
resins of gelatinous structure to be used for special inks, which
are themselves in a state of suspended gelation and which will

dry instantly by gelation

when exposed to the action of substances which are capable
of inducing gelation, either chemically or through surface
forces.

To translate this principle into actual practice, the sugges-
tion has been made to produce vehicles in a highly labile condition, by dissolving very viscous, low solubility resins of
gelatinous structure in oils at as low a temperature as 200° C.
and thinning the solution, if necessary, with volatile solvents.
Further, it has been suggested that the vehicle be ground with
inert pigments, producing an ink which is stable in the can,
will not gelatinize on the rollers of the press, but will dry
through gelatinization immediately when printed on paper
which is coated with a chemically reactive or surface active
pigment, such as zinc oxide.

Chapter VIII

The Application of Resins

The application of synthetic resins for surface coatings and printing inks is based on their particular properties. The selection of each type of resin for a given purpose is guided by its specific characteristics, as indicated by its physical and chemical property constants.

When pure phenol resins are incorporated into coatings or inks, the products are distinguished by weather resistance. Modified phenolics produce hardness and waterproofness, while modified maleics are noted for paleness of color and light stability. Copal-type synthetic resins produce outstanding drying and gloss characteristics.

Commercial synthetic resins, publicized in technical catalogs and bulletins, are identified by the general group to which they belong, and their properties are characterized in more detail by giving the values of color, acidity, melting point, viscosity and solubility and by describing the resin performance in surface coatings and printing inks. As a further assistance in the proper utilization of the resins, knowledge of their method of manufacture and chemical composition is desirable.

The last named information has been supplied for a number of representative coating and ink resins in the previous chapters. It is supplemented in the following discussion by useful suggestions for the practical application of resins for specific purposes. Due to the basically different requirements in the two fields—surface coatings and printing inks—the application of coating and ink resins is discussed separately. The comments are limited to the types dealt with in this volume, *i.e.* the acid- and alkali-condensed pure alkyl phenol resins, the rosin-modified bis phenol and alkyl phenol resins, the non-

233

esterified modified phenolics, the rosin-modified maleic and fumaric resins in their many varieties, and the copal-like synthetic resins.

RESIN APPLICATION IN SURFACE COATINGS

Among the many possible and current types of pure phenol resins, the acid- and alkali-condensed alkyl phenol types are discussed in detail. Very important resins of this group are the

Acid-condensed Para Tertiary Butyl Phenol Resins.

Their melting point may vary between 85° and 150° C., but usually lies between 125° and 135° C. The resins have an opalescent appearance; but give clear and pale varnishes of good color retention. The resin types of high melting point produce quick bodying and drying rates. On titration with alkali they show, like all acid-condensed alkyl phenol resins, distinct titration values which, however, do not indicate free acid and, therefore, do not impair their inertness with pigments.

The acid-condensed butyl phenol resins are soluble in aliphatic hydrocarbons. Therefore, in varnish making, straight mineral spirits can be used and no additions of xylol or other strong solvents are required. The resins combine with oils without foaming. Employing linseed oil, the unbodied oil should be used and the resin should be heated with all of the oil, to 580° F., and held there until the desired viscosity is obtained. Checking with linseed oil must be avoided, because it impairs the drying.

In wood oil containing varnishes, the wood oil is to be added as a chillback after the resin and the other oils are combined. The bodying of such wood oil varnishes should be carried out at 480° F. They quickly become gasproof and lose their tendency to skin.

The best drier composition for linseed oil combinations is 0.10% cobalt, 0.80% lead and 0.10% manganese, the percentage of the metal based on oil. If 50% of the oil consists of China wood oil, the drier content is reduced to one-half of these amounts.

Dehydrated castor oil does not lend itself to such varnishes, if they are longer in oil than 15 gallons, because of slow drying and aftertack.

The water and alkali resistance of varnishes, on the base of acid-condensed butyl phenol resins is high. For example, a straight 30 gallon linseed oil-varnish will pass the seven hour boiling water test; or a 30 gallon varnish containing half linseed oil and half wood oil will pass the alkali test of seven hours in 5% alkali solution.

The Kauri value of these varnishes is high. A straight 30 gallon linseed oil varnish has a Kauri value close to 90; if 5 gallons of wood oil are present, the value exceeds 100.

Acid-condensed butyl phenol resins produce excellent zinc chromate and other pigmented primers, and create finishes that are outstanding for their water, alkali and chemical resistance.

The group of

Acid-condensed Para Tertiary Amyl Phenol Resins

as a rule have lower melting points and somewhat higher transparency than the butyl phenol resins. They are distinguished by unusually high solubility and compatibility. Acid-condensed amyl phenol resins are soluble in petroleum ether, mineral spirits, or kerosene and also in alcohol. Such resin solutions are compatible with solutions of other resins in the same solvents. The resin, therefore, is the ideal material for cold cuts, designed to improve the water resistance of alkyd resin solutions, lacquers or spirit varnishes. Instead of using cold cuts of the straight resin, solutions of the resin, previously combined with small amounts of oil or plasticizers, can be used.

The acid-condensed amyl phenolics can easily be cooked with drying oils, such as China wood oil or oiticica oil, at top heats not exceeding 500° F. Such varnishes are gasproof and do not skin. To insure sufficient drying with linseed oil, unbodied linseed oil must be used, bodying resin and oil together in the kettle. Additions of China wood or oiticica oil are advisable. Dehydrated castor oil should be avoided, except in short oil varnishes or in baking finishes.

The resins can also be cooked directly into alkyd resins and such resin solutions stand practically infinite dilution with mineral spirits. Similar to the butyl phenol resins, they produce water, alkali and chemical resistance in the dried films, and impart to them pronounced elasticity, expressed by a high Kauri value.

The group of the acid-condensed alkyl phenol resins have the following applications in the field of surface coatings:

Aircraft wing and body finishes	*High Kauri reduction varnishes*
Alkali resistant coatings	*Hospital equipment finishes*
Alkyd resin modifications	*Lead paste primers*
Anti corrosive primers	*Locomotive finishes*
Boat topping paints	*Marine spar varnishes*
Bridge paints	*Mildew-proof fabrics*
Cable coatings	*Oil cloth finishes*
Electric motor finishes	*Passenger car outside paints*
Freight car finishes	*Ship superstructure paints*
High durability finishes	*Weather resistant finishes*

Zinc chromate primers

The interesting class of the

Alkali-condensed Alkyl Phenol Resins

is well represented by the para tertiary butyl phenol variety, the properties and uses of which are very similar to those of the para tertiary amyl phenol group.

The melting point of the alkali-condensed alkyl phenol

resins vary, as a rule, between 75° and 100° C. Their initial color is extremely pale and they keep their color in the dried varnish film much better than resins from the aromatic-substituted phenols. The slight apparent acidity of the resins originally present disappears when they are cooked with oil; the varnishes, therefore, are suitable for most pigmentations.

Alkali-condensed alkyl phenol resins are mildly heat reactive and their melting points increase when they are heated alone, until finally heat setting occurs. When heated with soft resins, like ester gum, they increase the melting point of such resins considerably. When heated with soft oils, like linseed oil, they increase the viscosity of such oils substantially. The last named procedure is important for practical varnish cooking. It requires very careful handling of the batches because it is accompanied by more than the usual foaming. The best technique is to bring the oil up to 350° F., add the resin slowly, stirring until it is completely dissolved, and heat to 425° F., holding the temperature until the foam has subsided. After the foam has disappeared the batch can be heat bodied at about 480° F., in the usual fashion. During the foaming period the resin loses about 5% in weight.

The alkali-condensed alkyl phenol resins have complete solubility in aliphatic hydrocarbons. Therefore, in varnish making, straight mineral spirits can be used and no addition of xylol or other strong solvent is required. The resins when cooked with China wood or oiticica oil dry quickly. When combined with linseed or dehydrated castor oil, satisfactory drying is obtainable only by increasing the amount of driers.

The resins impart high water and alkali resistance even to varnishes of great oil lengths, and make straight linseed oil varnishes very resistant. At the same time, such varnishes develop high Kauri values. For instance, a 25 gallon straight linseed oil varnish has a Kauri value of 80.

The class of alkali-condensed alkyl phenol resins is suggested for use in the following coatings:

Abrasive finishes   *Heat reactive compounds*
Boat varnishes   *Heat sealing compounds*
Brake linings   *Insulating varnishes*
Bus finishes   *Shade cloth finishes*
Chemical resistant coatings   *Ship bottom paints*
Concrete floor finishes   *Street car finishes*
Deck enamels   *Subway car finishes*
Dip tank enamels   *Swimming pool finishes*
Electrical equipment finishes   *Table top finishes*
Exterior enamels   *Tank car finishes*
Floor covering finishes   *Water resistant finishes*
Food container coatings   *Wiping enamels*
Gasoline pump enamels   *Wire insulation finishes*

The quantity of pure phenol resins used in the production of surface coatings is by far exceeded by the consumption of

Rosin-modified Phenol Resins.

All rosin-modified phenolics are available in two to three different grades of color and hardness, the color varying between F and WG, and the melting points between 110° and 170° C.

Their other properties also may change within wide limits due to the variation of several factors. The degree to which the resins are matured is one important factor; another possibility for variation consists in using gum rosin, wood rosin, polymerized or hydrogenated rosin, in employing various types of esterifying alcohol or in leaving the resins partially or entirely unesterified. Other changes can be made by the incorporation of maleic or fumaric compounds.

The most important factor in producing rosin-modified phenolics is the amount and the type of phenol formaldehyde condensate used. Practically only the alkali-condensed, and not the acid-catalyzed, phenolic bodies are employed for this purpose, the principle phenols being the alkyl substituted types of para tertiary butyl and amyl phenol and the bis phenol.

The resin types comprised under the heading of

Rosin-modified Alkyl Phenol Resins

are distinguished by unusually good solubility, even for the grades with high melting point and viscosity. They are completely soluble in mineral spirits, making the resins the first choice for cold cuts. The high degree of solubility also renders varnishes made with them very stable in the can.

Modified alkyl phenolics dissolve easily in all oils, thereby making the kettle procedure simple and fool-proof, and allowing the resins to be used safely as a chillback. This resin group also possesses good oil reactivity and, consequently, bodies fast in the kettle. For varnish making, only low top heats of approximately 550° F. are required. Because of easy kettle handling, they are the ideal material for combination with China wood oil or oiticica oil. They also render varnishes from these oils gasproof.

The drying characteristics of these resins are ideal for hard oils. For soft oils their drying accelerating effect, as a rule, is too weak. In accordance with their slow speed of saponification, they produce films of unusual alkali and water resistance. They also create high film elasticity, a factor which is of special importance for oiticica oil varnishes.

The various types of rosin-modified alkyl phenol resins have found use in surface coatings for the following purposes:

Acid resistant finishes
Aluminum vehicles
Artificial leather coatings
Bar top finishes
Chemical resistant coatings
China wood oil finishes
Cold cut petroleum solvent vehicles
Concrete floor finishes
Dip coating enamels

Foul weather fabrics
Fuel truck finishes
Gas holder paints
Hard oil varnishes
Household enamels
Motorcycle finishes
Porch enamels
Sanitary coatings
Shade cloth finishes

The large category of

Rosin-modified Bis Phenol Resins

has great practical importance, particularly the grades of medium color, melting points of 145-155° C. and viscosities of W to Z. These resins have sufficient color stability to make them suitable for use in enamels of all colors except white and very light tints. Their relatively low acidity makes them safe with most pigments and, if at least 50% of the oil used is linseed oil, even with zinc oxide. The high melting point of the hard grade of modified bis phenol resins offsets the softness of the oils with which they might be combined, and produces film hardness and abrasion resistance. The high viscosity of the resins, together with their good oil reactivity, accelerates the bodying speed in the varnish kettle. In spite of their high melting points and viscosities, these resins have sufficient solubility in mineral spirits to insure reliable stability of the varnishes on storage.

Cooking procedures are orthodox; as a rule a top heat of 580-590° F. should be applied. If low viscosity oils are used, the resin, with all of the oil, is heated together; if heavy oils are used, the cooking has to be done in steps. The resins should never be used as a chillback. Varnishes on the base of soft oils require small additions of hard oils, and their oil length should not be greater than 35 gallons. Driers recommended are 0.1% cobalt and 1% lead figured on the oil.

Rosin-modified bis phenol resins are difficult to saponify and, therefore, produce varnish films of high water and alkali resistance. The elasticity of dried coatings is satisfactory; for example, a 25 gallon straight linseed oil varnish has a Kauri value of not less than 40.

Recommended applications for resins in the category of rosin-modified bis phenol resins for the purpose of the production of coatings follow:

Architectural finishes
Barn paints
Brush enamels

Colored enamels
Communication equipment
  finishes

Conveyor paints
Crane paints
Dairy enamels
Engine enamels
Farm machinery finishes
Farm tractor finishes
Floor enamels
Floor varnishes
General purpose vehicles
Grinding vehicles
Household enamels
Implement finishes
Industrial instrument finishes
Industrial tractor finishes
Locker finishes
Machine tool finishes
Office equipment finishes

Passenger car finishes
Pump enamels
Railroad equipment finishes
Road sign finishes
Shop coats
Spray enamels
Telegraph equipment finishes
Telephone equipment finishes
Trade sales finishes
Trailer finishes
Tractor paints
Transportation equipment finishes
Trim paints
Truck enamels
Wall covering finishes
Wheel enamels

The relatively small but important family of the

Non-esterified Modified Phenolics

are produced with various types of phenol-formaldehyde condensates such as those of U.S.P. phenol, cresols, butyl phenol,
but mostly of bis phenol. The non-esterfied phenolics have
constants, similar to those of the esterified types; however,
are necessarily high in acidity, the acid values ranging between 100 and 130, which somewhat restricts the pigmenta-
tion of varnishes produced with them. Their phenol content
is high, resulting in some after-yellowing of the dried varnish
film. Non-esterified phenolics exceed normal phenolics in
their drying speed to a remarkable extent, and in their power
to cause through-hardening of the film. The accelerated drying
effect is particularly great on linseed oil and somewhat less
pronounced on dehydrated castor oil.

In cooking these resins into varnishes, low viscosity oils
should be employed, and the amount of driers should be
adapted to the type of oils used. In case of varnishes of more
than 15 gallons oil length, the resin is heated with part of the

oil first and further additions are made in steps, reheating each time to top heat. The resins are ideal for straight China wood oil and oiticica oil varnishes, because their high acidity prevents gelatinization and allows complete gasproofing. The water resistance of their varnishes is good. In line with the through-drying tendencies of the resin, Kauri values are low.

Non-esterified, rosin-modified phenolics are distinguished by an unusually high tolerance for alcohol.

Members of the family of non-esterified modified phenolics find useful application in the following finishes:

Abrasive finishes	*Nonskinning vehicles*
Athletic equipment finishes	*Office furniture finishes*
Automobile primers	*Quick drying finishes*
Automobile surfacers	*Restaurant table top finishes*
Baking finishes	*Rubbing varnishes*
Bowling alley finishes	*Sanding sealers*
Chassis blacks	*Short oil China wood oil varnishes*
Factory furniture finishes	*Table top finishes*
Fender enamels	*Under coats*
Long-oil China wood oil varnishes	*Wrinkle finishes*
Mopping varnishes	

The large group of

The Varnish Maleic Resins

are distinguished by a high degree of paleness and color stability, which withstand baking temperatures to a remarkable extent. A great number of different grades are produced by changing various factors as, for instance, the type of the rosin used, or the nature and the amount of the esterifying alcohol employed, particularly glycerine and the pentaerythritols. Other variations are due to the use of differing amounts of maleic or fumaric compounds separately or in combination, or to a more or less thorough maturing of the resins. It is also possible to incorporate phenolics, which produce further variations.

In this way the class of varnish maleics is built up, yielding individual resins, varying in acidity from 10 to 40, in melting point from 120-155° C., in viscosity from *F* to *Z*, and in solubility, from types which are completely soluble in aliphatic hydrocarbons, to those which are soluble only in aromatic hydrocarbons. Accordingly, the solubility in oils varies within wide limits, some resin types dissolving in bodied oils at very low temperatures, and others going into solution only at the high temperature of more than 550° F.

In varnish cooking, the maleics show little reactivity with oils and body comparatively slowly. On storage the maleic varnishes have a tendency to gain viscosity, which may lead to gel formation. Maleic varnishes dry satisfactorily when freshly made, but show a decided loss in drying speed on storage. This deficiency is little noticeable in varnishes of an oil length shorter than ten gallons, and is negligible in all baking finishes. Varnishes made with high melting maleics possess good hardness of the dried film, even when soft oils are used. The water and alkali resistance of maleic varnish films is low, in accordance with the pronounced saponifiability of the resins.

The many coating purposes for which the group of varnish maleic resins is used are enumerated in the following list:

Architectural finishes
Automotive surfacers
Baking finishes
Bedstead finishes
Cardboard coatings
Carton coatings
Coated fabric finishes
Container coatings
Color stable varnishes and enamels
Fibre container finishes
Flat wall paints
Flat wall primers
Food machinery paints
Furniture varnishes
Grinding vehicles

High viscosity varnishes
Hospital paints
Metal cabinet finishes
Mill whites
Optical instrument finishes
Pastel enamels
Pharmaceutical machinery paints
Refrigerator paints
Roller coat application finishes
Scientific instrument finishes
Stucco paints
Toy finishes
Venetian blind finishes
Wall board coatings
Zone marking paints

The various members of the family of

The Lacquer Maleic Resins

are composed and manufactured similar to varnish maleics, though in such a way that they are compatible with nitro-cellulose in a wide variety of cotton to resin ratios. The degree of compatibility is judged, not from the clearness of the lacquer solution, but from the transparency of the dried lacquer film. Certain lacquer maleics are also compatible with ethyl cellulose.

The color of these resin types varies between WG and M on the rosin scale; their color stability in the lacquer film is excellent. Their acid value, varying between 20 and 40, is sufficiently low so as not to influence cotton viscosity or pigment stability. The melting point, ranging from 120-150° C., insures hard finishes, suitable for easy rubbing and polishing, as well as for sharp and clear sanding, even in the presence of a plasticizer. Their viscosity is of medium range, permitting high resin concentration in lacquers. The low viscosity of lacquer maleics, as a rule, is combined with an exceptionally high tolerance for petroleum solvents, both properties making it possible to increase gloss and decrease costs at the same time. In spite of their hardness, lacquer maleics have a certain amount of elasticity. Therefore, lacquer films, even with a high percentage of resin, and when applied on wood, show no shrinkage several days after polishing and give good results in the cold check cycle. The resins also possess good resistance to alcohol, rubbing oils and greases.

Lacquer maleic resins are used for the type of finishes which are given in this list:

Automotive type enamels	*Collapsible tube coatings*
Baby carriage finishes	*Color stable lacquers*
Bicycle finishes	*Container liners*
Casket finishes	*Ethyl cellulose finishes*
Cloth coatings	*Flexible lacquers*
Coated fabric finishes	*General utility lacquers*

Kitchen equipment finishes
Label lacquers
License plate finishes
Lacquer enamels
Lighting fixture finishes
Metal lacquers
Musical instrument finishes
Nail polishes
Nitrocellulose finishes
Radio cabinet finishes

Sanding sealers
Scale finishes
Sealer lacquers
Shoe linings
Textile coatings
Tin decorative finishes
Wood fillers
Wood lacquers
Wood primers

Lacquer maleics are insoluble in alcohol, but there is a definite need for maleics which are freely soluble in ethyl alcohol. Such

Alcohol-soluble Maleic Resins

are available in the form of resins with relatively high acidity of about 150, and with melting points of about 125° C. They contain mostly substantial percentages of fumaric, instead of maleic compounds, which is an advantage in their practical application, because fumaric acid is much less toxic than maleic acid.

Due to high acidity, the resins will reduce the viscosity of nitrocellulose and, therefore, as a rule, are not recommended for nitrocellulose lacquers. In special compositions, for instance, in the case of certain metal finishes, the high acidity may act in favor of good adhesion.

The resin solution in alcohol is miscible with alcohol solutions of natural gums. The resins are not a substitute for the natural gums, but have merits of their own in places where they are being used, due to their uniformity and cleanliness.

The alcoholic solutions of the maleic types under discussion are compatible with ethyl cellulose and zein solutions. Both substances impart higher viscosity and more tackfree drying to the maleic. Ethyl cellulose, in addition, conveys toughness to the film. Zein makes the film insoluble in petroleum solvents. Therefore, the resin-zein combination reduces bleeding when used as sealer or size under paints which contain mineral spirits.

Alcohol-soluble maleics or fumarics are applied for the following purposes:

Adhesives	*Glycol solutions*
Alcohol solutions	*Leather coatings*
Artificial leather coatings	*Mazein formulations*
Automobile primers	*Paper coatings*
Cardboard coatings	*Shoe adhesives*
Cements	*Spirit varnishes*
Ethyl cellulose finishes	*Tire retread combinations*
Flat wall sizes	*Wood sealers*

The important resin types summarized under the term of

Copal-type Synthetic Resins

are distinguished by unusual property combinations which originate from the unique process of gelling and degelling, used in their manufacture. The resin properties vary with changes in the processing and depend on the chemical nature of the raw material, which may be either of the phenolic, the maleic, the natural copal type or of combinations of these types.

The color of copal-type synthetics varies from a grade darker than D up to color grades of about K-M. Their acidity fluctuates between 10 and 40 and their melting point between 140° and 170° C., with corresponding fluctuations in viscosity. The resin class is distinguished by molecular homogeneity and uniformity, which in turn favors solubility.

Due to their good solubility, the resins are usable for cold cuts in many types of aliphatic hydrocarbons, and are well suited to the modification of alkyd resins, resulting in an improvement of through-drying and gloss retention. The same solubility characteristic causes the resins to dissolve easily and at low temperature in bodied oils.

All copal-type synthetics are oil reactive and, therefore, permit fast cooking schedules in varnish making. As a rule, bodied oils are used and all of the resin and the oil are heated together to a temperature of about 575° F. In preparing a 25 gallon varnish of *E-F* body with 50% solids in mineral spirits, a cooking time of 60 minutes is required when a *Z* viscosity linseed oil is used, and a cooking time of 20 minutes is required when a Z_3 viscosity, dehydrated castor oil, is employed. Copal-type synthetics can be cooked with oils to much higher viscosities than phenolics or maleics, without running into the danger of gelatinization. The heating loss is relatively small, because of the heat stability of this resin class.

The copal-type synthetics are the quickest drying resins available. They allow, therefore, high amounts of linseed oil and comparatively low drier contents. Their varnishes are distinguished by pigment stability, non-skinning properties and the absence of after-bodying. Their water resistance is close to that of varnishes made with high grade modified phenolics.

As appears from the foregoing description, the various resin types in the category of copal-like synthetics are many sided in their field of application. A list of recommended end uses follows:

Agricultural implement finishes
Alkyd resin modifications
Architectural finishes
Blending varnishes
Brewery finishes
Can stable paints
Closure finishes
Cold cut solutions
Drum coatings
Four-hour enamels
Fuel wagon finishes
Hardware finishes
Highway marking paints
House paints

Industrial finishes
Laundry equipment finishes
Metal furniture finishes
Operating room enamels
Passenger car inside paints
Radiator finishes
Refrigerator enamels
Safety equipment finishes
Shelf goods
Ship inside paints
Soft oil varnishes
Textile machinery paints
Traffic paints
Varnish stains

RESIN APPLICATION IN PRINTING INKS

In the field of practical application of printing ink resins, the rosin-modified phenolics are the most important resins, with the pure phenolics playing only a minor role. Among the rosin-modified phenolics, the bis phenol and the alkyl phenol varieties are of particular interest. In the large group of

Rosin-modified Bis Phenol Resins

are found a number of resin types, *i.e.* those of high melting point and viscosity, which possess all the properties required for the manufacture of printing ink products, especially overprint varnishes and gloss inks.

Their color is sufficiently pale initially, and adequately stable in the film on drying, for use in most ink vehicles, though they have to be employed with discretion in light colored overprint varnishes. Their acidity is low enough to insure neutrality with pigments, and the acidity is of a type that does not cause a loss of drying ability during storage, as occurs with maleic resins.

The resin types in question have high melting points, producing rubproof and mar-resistant finishes. They possess viscosities of a degree best suited to printing ink production. Ink resins generally must not have viscosities lower than U-V, determined in a solution of 60% resin in xylol on the Gardner scale, and not higher than Z-Z_1, the optimum viscosity being about X. Resins with lower than U viscosity produce ink vehicles too tacky for good printability; such vehicles also have poor gloss in overprint varnishes and gloss inks and, with certain pigments, develop pronounced bronzing effects. Resins with higher than Z_1 viscosity usually require too much kerosene or litho oil to obtain printability, so that the materials lose gloss after printing, due to evaporation or penetration.

The solubility of rosin-modified bis phenol ink resins is limited. When dissolving the resins in cuts of hydro carbons, customary for heat-set inks, additions of strong solvents, such as carbitol, are required to obtain complete solution. When dissolving the resins in litho oils, temperatures of 400 to 500° F. are necessary. The solutions thus produced are distinguished by a minimum of penetration into the paper.

The oxidation drying of prints containing modified bis phenol resins proceeds quicker than that of prints containing maleics, and the gloss of the dried print is superior to that of inks based on other types of ink resins. The final prints are distinguished by water, alcohol and alkali resistance, and by a peculiar lack of odor.

The class of rosin-modified phenolics is used for the following printing ink preparations:

Absorbent inks	*Label inks*
Alkali-proof inks	*Ledger inks*
Bond paper inks	*Lithographic inks*
Carbon inks	*Offset inks*
Cotton bag inks	*Odorless inks*
Flexible inks	*Overprint varnishes*
Flour bag inks	*Rubproof inks*
Gloss inks	*Scratch proof inks*
High gloss inks	*Sugar bag inks*

The very interesting category of

Modified Alkyl Phenol Resins

contains in its upper viscosity brackets, ink resin grades both of the butyl phenol and amyl phenol type which are outstanding, due to an unusual combination of great hardness and high solubility, properties which normally are inversely proportional to each other.

The melting point of these resins approaches closely 170° C. *i.e.* a degree of hardness which in most other resin types, especially in modified bis phenol resins, carries with it an impractically high viscosity. In spite of these high melting points, the resins are easily soluble, both in bodied linseed oil and in volatile solvents. On heating with litho oils they go into solution at temperatures which are 100° F. lower than the temperatures required for bis phenol resins.

Alkyl phenol resins dissolve completely in cuts of mineral oils of even the lowest Kauri-butanol value at practical concentrations, without precipitation of the resin on standing. Their solution in kerosene, for instance, can be thinned with kerosene down to 10 to 25% resin concentration and still remain stable, which is an indication of extreme solubility. Such solutions can also be mixed, without decomposition, with solutions of low viscosity resins, in cases where it seems desirable to improve the flow of an ink.

All these characteristics make the modified alkyl phenolics the ideal ink resins for heat-set inks. But they have special merits also in many other printing inks. The following list cites a number of typical examples:

Alkali-proof inks   *Letter press inks*
Bottle cap inks   *Linoleum inks*
Chemically resistant inks   *Metallic inks*
Gravure inks   *Metal foil inks*
Heat-set inks   *Moisture resistant inks*
High speed magazine inks   *Soap wrapper inks*
Instant drying inks   *Synthetic litho inks*
Kerosene solutions   *Waterproof inks*

The manifold and large class of

Rosin-modified Maleic Resins

for printing inks is distinguished by initially pale color and by their ability to retain a light color after drying of the ink film, providing the ink vehicle is not overloaded with driers and no phenolic additions have been made.

The melting points of maleic resins for printing inks are

comparatively high, *i.e.* 145° to 165° C., which act in favor of the ink's hardness, rubproofness and scratch resistance. In spite of relatively small fluctuations in melting points, the viscosities of maleic ink resins may vary within wide limits, *i.e.* from N to Z_3, mostly as a consequence of a change in the type of esterifying alcohol used in their manufacture.

Viscosities lower than W cause lack of gloss, pronounced penetration, excessive tackiness and, in certain instances, bronzing. The optimum viscosity for obtaining printability and gloss is about Z, as determined on the Gardner scale in 60% xylol solution. This measurement is directly proportional to the viscosity of resin solutions in linseed oil, determined by the Stormer viscometer. Resins of higher viscosities are recommended for practical applications only in special instances; for example, in cases where it is desired to offer the formulator of overprint varnishes and gloss inks more than the usual opportunity for varying oil viscosities and kerosene content, in order to meet the requirements of gloss and non-penetration.

The solubility of normal ink maleics varies widely. Expressing the degree of solubility by the minimum temperature at which the resins render clear solutions with Z body linseed oil, the clearing points vary between 200° F. and 550° F. These practical variations have become even larger, since it is possible, by means of the maturing process, to transform low solubility types into high solubility grades, at the same time increasing the hardness without changing the viscosity.

As a rule, high solubility is desirable for practical uses, because it eases kettle handling, favors stability of the clear ink vehicle on storage, and counteracts pigment reactivities which may lead to livering of the ink. In exceptional cases, resins of low solubility are required. Such resins are usually of the excessively high viscosity variety with a gelatinous structure, suggested for use in the peculiar types of inks which dry by gelation. If resins with gel structure are heated with oil up to temperatures of 585° F., the gelatinous matter is destroyed.

The speed of drying of inks, based on modified maleics, is only slightly lower than that of inks made with modified phenolics, and is satisfactory for all practical purposes. For instance, with the right formulation, overprint varnishes will show no offsetting when stacked immediately after printing. However, in common with all maleic resins, the ink maleics gradually inactivate drier metals and, therefore, maleic resin-containing printing inks may lose their drying strength when stored over a long period of time.

The maleic resin group is suggested for the following applications in printing ink manufacture:

Can label inks	*Overprint varnishes*
Cigarette label inks	*Rotogravure inks*
Comic color inks	*Stencil inks*
Embossing inks	*Stamping inks*
Food label inks	*Tin foil inks*
Gloss inks	*Typographic inks*
Gravure inks	*Wrapper inks*
Label inks	

Another interesting group of maleic type resins is the class of

Glycol-soluble Maleic Resins

designed for steam-setting inks. They generally contain a large amount of dibasic acid, a good part of which may be the relatively non-toxic fumaric acid. All are of the non-esterified type and, therefore, have very high acid values of close to 300. Their melting points are as high as 160° C., which produces tack-free ink layers. They are completely and readily soluble in diethylene glycol, the 40% resin solution having viscosities of about U. The diethylene glycol solution possesses a considerable tolerance for water. This is desirable to avoid premature decomposition on the rollers of inks made with such solutions, due to the humidity of the press room. Viewed from this angle, a water tolerance of 25% is desirable.

The determination of water tolerance is carried out as follows: A 40% solution of the resin in diethylene glycol is prepared by heating the two substances together to about 300°F. After cooling, 100 grams of the solution are introduced into a small beaker and agitated by an electric laboratory mixer. 5 c.c. of distilled water are titrated into it in a steady flow and agitation is continued for several minutes. When a smooth homogeneous emulsion is obtained, the agitation is stopped and the liquid is allowed to stand until it clears. The same procedure is repeated, with the addition of 5 c.c. of water each time, until the mixture, after the usual clearing up period, begins to retain a distinct cloudiness. The amount of water added at this point is the percentage of tolerance. It must be understood that the test is only of relative value, giving the ink maker a measure of comparison.

The resins are also completely soluble in alcohol and, as a result, lend themselves to evaporative-type inks, containing mainly alcohol as solvent. In order to insure stability of such solutions, small additions of other solvents, such as coal-tar hydrocarbons, are sometimes made.

The glycol-soluble maleic type resins are primarily designed for steam-set inks, though their field of application actually is wider, as indicated by the following examples:

Aniline inks	*Laundry-marking inks*
Cellophane inks	*Steam-set inks*
Celluloid inks	*Textile-marking inks*
Cold-set inks	*Water-set inks*
Fabric marking inks	*Wax-set inks*
Heat-set inks	

The comparatively young and very unique resin family of

Copal-type Synthetic Resins

contains among its higher viscosity members a number of outstanding ink resins, possessing characteristics which make them particularly suitable for the purpose. The low acidity insures pigment stability, which is clearly superior to that of both phenolics and maleics. The viscosity of the hard grade types lies in the range that produces an optimum of gloss. Their melting point is high, creating scratchproof and rub-resistant prints. Their good solubility makes it possible to employ ample amounts of kerosene.

The resins accelerate oxidation drying. No loss in drying properties during storage is experienced, nor is any skin formation observed. Ink vehicles based on copal-type synthetics dry quickly and reliably even in black inks. The dried film has an exceptional slip and more than customary rub resistance. Its gloss is comparable to that of the high viscosity modified phenolics; it is of a smooth type, whereas phenolics produce a more specular type of gloss. Combinations of these two resins give special effects.

Penetration of copal-type resin vehicles is low; it increases, of course, with the amount of oil relative to the resin amount, though copal-type synthetics tolerate a higher than normal quantity of oil.

The principal uses of the group of copal-type synthetic resins in ink manufacture follow:

Aluminum inks	*Metal decorating inks*
Bag inks	*Metallic inks*
Bread wrapper inks	*Non-rub inks*
Gloss inks	*Non-scratch inks*
High speed rotary press inks	*Offset inks*
Intaglio printing ink	*Overprint varnishes*
Magazine color inks	*Rub-resisting inks*

The previous survey gives an idea of the manifold uses of the resins discussed in this book for the manufacture of surface coatings and printing inks.

In addition, there exists a number of

other resin uses

which are mentioned briefly. The resins, for instance, have an important place in flooring materials, such as linoleum, floor tiles and other floor coverings. They are useful in certain paper treatments as components of paper sizing, impregnating, waterproofing, greaseproofing and stiffening agents. The resins have a wide field of application in adhesives and cements, both of the hot-melt and solvent types for binding cork, paper, wood, etc.; they are also widely used for electrical insulation purposes in impregnating and filling compounds. The resins discussed in this study are, furthermore, useful in textile manufacturing as components for waterproofing, flame and rotproofing of tents, awnings, sails, tarpaulins, especially in combination with alkyd resins. They can also be incorporated into water emulsions, after being combined with sufficient amounts of thin oil to yield flowing resin-oil compounds.

Surveying the entire field of the application of resins, it is surprising to note the large number and varieties of uses for the resins under discussion. They actually have found practical application for several hundred different purposes.

Chapter IX

Machinery and Equipment

In order to produce custom-built resins, with every detail of their physical and chemical characteristics predetermined, and with all specifications met exactly in the finished resins, special machinery and equipment are required. The use of ordinary varnish kettles has been repeatedly suggested and has often been tried out for resin making. The products thus obtained are inferior for obvious reasons. Varnish kettles are heated by direct fires, with oversized flames acting on relatively small heating areas. The result is partial overheating at the kettle bottom and at the kettle walls, causing granulation and seediness, scorching and charring. The customary hand agitation, or stirring by portable mechanical agitators, is insufficient to counteract the uneven heat input, and also is generally inadequate to cope with heavy foaming.

Orthodox varnish kettles have no reflux condensers capable of retaining valuable volatile ingredients, such as glycerine. Even if a special top construction is installed, using a long pipe as an air cooled condenser, a great loss in glycerine, maleic anhydride or other volatile resin reactants is unavoidable, rendering the process uneconomical. Neither are varnish kettles equipped with vacuum to draw off the decomposition products which, if left in the resins, are detrimental to their hardness, drying, resistance and pigment stability.

The main reason for the inferiority of coating and ink

resins produced in varnish kettles

lies in the fact that insufficient time is allowed for the resin-forming reactions. None of the reactions occurring in resin production are of the instantaneous type, such as the sudden interaction between silver nitrate and sodium chloride in their aqueous solutions. All resin-producing reactions are slow and most of them require more than eight hours for completion, the ultimate in the time usually available in varnish kettles. If the time factor is not given sufficient consideration, poor quality resins will be the result. High class resins, therefore, are made under very long time cycles, giving the components full opportunity for complete reaction. The time factor is of particular importance in the case of resin maturing, when the kettle contents are subjected to a long period of continuous and uniform heating.

The equipment and machinery necessary for the production of coating and ink resins is of a highly specialized nature. Every item of the total assembly is adapted to its specialized purpose; even the smallest part is not allowed to be "just good enough," but is constructed to best suit its particular objective. Such an assembly is not designed overnight, but evolves only through years of production experience. Often the correct construction details are only learned the hard way; that is to say, by making all the mistakes that can possibly be made first, and then gradually eliminating them.

A survey of the

principles of engineering

which govern resin production is of general interest to both resin producers and resin users. Engineering of machinery and equipment concern the design and material of the kettles, their heating and cooling, and means of agitation. They concern refluxing and condensing, pressure and vacuum, loading and unloading, and last, but by no means least, the instruments and devices for production control and safety.

Various metals are available for resin kettles. One of the best is stainless steel of a type containing 18% nickel and 8% chromium, with usually no molybdenum present. Clad stainless steel is usable for the shell and head plates, though not for the bottom. Stainless steel is highly resistant to organic acids, even at temperatures up to 320° C. It is free from attack by liquid acidic resins, and only very slightly pitted by extended action of acid vapors in the presence of oxygen and water. On the other hand, stainless steel is plainly corroded by mineral acids, such as hydrochloric acid, even in concentrations of less than one-tenth of one per cent.

Other excellent

metals for resin kettles

are nickel, nickel copper and nickel chromium alloys. All of these are more quickly corroded than stainless steel and the traces of nickel metal which dissolve in the resin due to the corrosion may have adverse effects on products and processes. For instance, cases are on record in which the nickel salts accelerate the decomposition of resinous esters.

Aluminum has lost its established place as building material for kettle walls and kettle tops. The metal softens at temperatures around 300° C. so pronouncedly, that unless the walls are excessively thick, the kettle shell will not withstand the pressure created by vacuum and will be pressed together partially or even collapse totally. However, there may be possibilities in the new aluminum magnesium alloys for resin kettles, because they are more resistant than straight aluminum. The bottoms of aluminum kettles have generally been copper, but this formerly approved combination has also been practically abandoned. The same is true of the use of copper as kettle material because of its low resistance to acidic resins.

In judging the suitability of the various metals for the building of resin kettles, the importance of the relative speed of heat conduction of different metals is sometimes emphasized. It is true that the heat conductivity of aluminum is three times, and that of copper four times higher than that of stainless steel, but the distance which the heat actually has to travel in the metal, *i.e.*, the distance from the inner to the outer surface, or the thickness of the kettle wall, is so small that differences in heat conductivity are thereby rendered negligible. But even if they had a bearing on heating speed, their influence would be counteracted and practically compensated for by the fact that the metals of low tensile strength, such as aluminum and copper, require much greater wall thicknesses than metals of high tensile strength like stainless steel. To equal the strength of a ⅜-inch stainless steel wall, a thickness of ¾-inch is required for copper and 1-inch for aluminum.

The efficiency of

heat transfer

through the kettle wall does not depend entirely on the thermal conductivity of the wall metal, but also depends on the cleanliness of the wall surfaces both inside and outside, *i.e.* its freedom from foreign matter. Soot formation at the outer kettle wall or the building up of a gelatinous or hard resinous layer on the inner surface may delay heat transfer to a dangerously high degree.

Glass-lined kettles are the exception in the production of coating and ink resins, and are required only in cases where inorganic acids are used in certain stages of the manufacturing process.

The shapes of production kettles vary little under practical conditions. Bottoms and heads are built in dish form, details being predicated on the fabricating equipment of the kettle builder and the type of metal used. The shell is mostly cylindrical and only in exceptional cases slightly conical. As a rule the diameter of the shell is approximately equal to its height. However, if good agitation is provided, shell heights which considerably exceed their diameter are perfectly feasible and in certain cases, even preferred as, for instance, for the purpose of ester gum manufacture.

Agitation is an important factor in all kettle design, because the heat conductivity of all resins is poor. To insure quick heat distribution, mechanical movement of the heated contents, by means of efficient agitators, is necessary.

The efficiency of stirring

depends on the details of the agitator, its speed of revolution, the adequate arrangement of baffle plates, etc. Strong, preferably oversized motors, are desirable. Suggestions have been made to place the agitator shaft in the kettle off center, to increase efficiency. In certain copal kettles and in equipment for producing heat-set resins, additional agitator blades are arranged to closely scrape the kettle bottom and the walls.

Particularly efficient agitation is required when the kettle heat is rapidly increased or when there is a large temperature differential between the zones inside and outside the kettle wall and bottom. This differential is especially large in directly fired kettles. Without efficient agitation, the kettle content will coke and carbonize on the walls and bottom of such equipment, and the metal will be destroyed through overheating with possibly disastrous results.

With increasing resin demands the sizes of resin kettles have grown gradually and have reached, in special cases, the dimensions of five to ten thousand-gallon capacity. Theoretically there is no upper

limit to kettle sizes.

But a very strict practical limitation presents itself in the kettle size for the production of coating and ink resins, because of the fact that the time required for heating and cooling increases with the resin load, and must not exceed a certain upper limit. In both heating and cooling procedures the heat exchange occurs at the surface of the kettle wall and bottom, or at the surface of cooling coils placed inside the kettle. The speed of heating or cooling is a function of the ratio of the resin surface, active in the heat exchange, to the poundage of the resin.

To study these conditions in detail, a survey was made of the speed of heating in various kettle sizes recording, at the same time, the resin load in pounds, the heating surface, and the heating time. For this investigation four different kettle sizes were chosen: (1) a kettle of approximately 1000-gallon total capacity, a size predominant in the trade and favored by smaller producers; (2) a 2000-gallon kettle representing an average size used in resin manufacture; (3) a kettle of nearly 4000-gallon capacity, which is in actual, though not wide-spread, use; (4) a vessel of nearly 9000 gallon total content, which is a very unusual size for current production, although 10,000-gallon kettles are in the offing.

For the purpose of comparing the

efficiency of the four kettles

they were all assumed to be of similar design, and built of stainless steel, the diameter of the shell being approximately equal to the height of the straight shell, bottom and top being fabricated in the usual dish form. For purposes of comparison, it was also assumed that the same type heating system was used, with the same degree of effective heat and the same temperature differential between the inside and outside zone of kettle wall and bottom, causing the same heat input per square foot of heating surface from the outside of the kettle. The corresponding area inside the kettle was assumed to be covered completely by the resin load. Agitation was considered to be equally efficient in all four kettle sizes, which is entirely feasible with present day engineering, even in the large vessels. The resin referred to was a modified phenolic, with relatively low glycerine content, weighing, while liquid, about nine pounds per gallon.

The results of this survey on the speed of heating in various kettle sizes are reported in *Table 22*.

The data compiled are very instructive. Commenting first

Table 22. Speed of Temperature Rise in Various Kettle Sizes

Approximate Total Capacity of Kettle	*850 Gallons*	*2000 Gallons*	*3600 Gallons*	*8500 Gallons*
Diameter of kettle	5 feet	6½ feet	8 feet	11 feet
Resin load in kettle	5000 lbs.	12000 lbs.	22000 lbs.	51000 lbs.
Surface area covered by resin	75 sq. feet	133 sq. feet	195 sq. feet	380 sq. feet
Ratio of resin load to heating surface	67	90	112	135
Time to heat from 160° to 280° C.	6 hours	8 hours	10 hours	12 hours

on the diameter of the four kettles, the interesting fact must
be emphasized that by adding one and one-half feet to the

kettle diameter

and the height of the shell, the total capacity is about doubled
in the range of one thousand to four thousand-gallon kettles.
It also appears from a comparison of the smallest with the
largest vessel that, by doubling kettle diameter and height, its
total content is increased nearly ten times.

The poundage figures given for the resin load are practical
production loads, amounting to about 67% of the total kettle
capacity. With this load the kettles are filled up to two-thirds
of the straight shell, a two thousand-gallon kettle carrying
about twelve thousand pounds, a nine thousand-gallon kettle
carrying about fifty thousand pounds of resin. Accordingly,
the figures for the surface area given in the table cover the sum
total of the inner surface of the dish bottom, and two-thirds of
the surface of the straight shell, all figures expressed in square
feet. Comparing the increase of the

heated surface area

covered by resin, with the increase of the resin load in pounds
in the four kettles, it appears that the surface area grows

slower than the poundage. For instance, comparing the smallest with the largest kettle in the chart, the surface of the latter is five times larger, whereas its poundage is ten times larger than the former. This relationship cannot be altered in the kettles for the production of coating and ink resins, because it is not possible to design supplemental heat exchange surfaces, as is feasible in the heating of oils.

The ratio of resin load to heating surface is of great practical importance, because it governs the time required to heat the various kettles. Heating speed is inversely proportional to the load and directly proportional to the surface. The figures given in the chart indicate the number of pounds of resin subjected to heating by one square foot of heating surface. This amount is 67 pounds in a small kettle of 850-gallon content and 135 pounds in a large kettle of 8500-gallon capacity. Obviously the smaller poundage is heated quicker than the larger poundage, and the time required to increase the kettle temperature by a certain number of degrees for a particular kettle size can be derived from the data valid for a known kettle size by using its quotient of load to surface. In this way

the heating times

given in the bottom horizontal line of the table are determined for the three sizes of 850, 3600- and 8500-gallon total capacity, applying as base figure the well established data for a 2000-gallon kettle, in which 12000 pounds of a modified phenolic, undergoing processing, are heated up from 160°-280° C. at a speed of 15° C. per hour. This heating speed can be obtained without local overheating of the wall and bottom zones of the resin load, provided the mass is efficiently agitated. The heating speed is reduced in case of heavy refluxing of glycerine, or may be accelerated if exothermic reactions take place.

The starting temperature of 160° C. is chosen, in order to eliminate the influence of the latent heat of fusion in these comparative considerations, in accordance with the production practice of pumping or sucking the liquid rosin into the kettle.

When, instead of the rosin-modified phenolic resin, other hard resins, such as maleics or copal-type synthetics are used, similar results are obtained, because the specific heat of these resins is the same. Incidentally, specific heats of hard resins are very low, and amount to only about one-half that of water.

The thermal conditions in a resin production kettle are of a composite nature, consisting of endothermic, exothermic, and such reactions which neither consume nor develop heat. The most

important thermal factor

is esterification, which consumes heat. Its endothermic effect is multiplied by the action of reflux condensers when glycols or glycerine are used. These indirectly cool down the kettle content severely. Exothermic reactions are the exception in resin kettles and are avoided if possible. Normal polymerization of hard coating and ink resins does not develop more heat than is consumed by distilling off decomposition products, so that both factors balance. It is only when the resin begins to gelatinize that the temperature starts to rise by exothermic reactions which, under certain circumstances, might easily get out of control.

Comparing the reported heating times of the four kettles of increased diameters, it follows that the time of heating increases with the resin load though not in direct proportion, because theoretically the weight increases as the cube, and the heating surface increases as the square, of the kettle diameter. The table actually shows that the heating time increases considerably slower with the kettle size than with the load, to the extent that a ten times higher load requires only twice as much time to heat. Nevertheless, at a load of about 50000 pounds, a heating time of 12 hours is reached which, for most production schedules, seems to be the upper allowable limit of time. Therefore, on the strength of the survey, it can be stated that, for the practical purpose of producing hard coating and ink resins, kettle sizes larger than 10000 gallons are not recommended.

The recommendation of this maximum kettle size is based on a heating time of eight hours for a 2000 gallon kettle. Any other base figure can be chosen without changing the relationship of the various factors. If, for instance, a resinous material and a type of equipment is chosen which allows double the heating speed, the practical maximum resin load can be increased accordingly.

The same argumentation that puts a limitation on kettle sizes due to excessively long heating times, is even more true if based on cooling times. Cooling of a kettle is just as important as heating and, as a rule, is more difficult to carry out. Practically all

possible heating systems

both with direct or indirect heat, are used for resin kettles, the heating medium being coal, oil, gas or electricity. The problem in all cases is to design the heating equipment in such a way as to obtain the maximum heat transfer without local overheating of the kettle content. Powerful and efficient agitation is necessary in all cases.

The methods of direct heating are based on burning coal, oil or gas, or on applying electricity. Using coal, oil or gas, special care must be taken that local overheating of the kettle wall is prevented. For this purpose automatic stokers with a forced draft system, used for coal or coke firing, or well regulated and adjustable burners, used for oil or gas, have to be located far enough away from the kettle to avoid direct contact of the flame with kettle bottom and shell. Combustion chambers and flues have to be so constructed that excessive accumulation of heat is avoided in the furnace walls, which makes temperature control and cooling operations difficult. The ceramic industry has developed refractories of low heat storage capacity and low thermal conductivity for this purpose.

Electrical heating is carried out in various ways. Heating by the method of container resistance or by means of immersion heaters is not suitable for resin production. Sometimes kettles are heated by electrical elements directly clamped to the kettle wall and bottom, transferring heat by conduction, a method which is liable to produce hot spots, causing overheating. In the best type of electrical heating system the

heating elements are arranged in a radiant furnace

around the kettle. This system produces very uniform and gentle heat and allows extremely fine temperature control. In addition, very little heat is lost in this arrangement, because the ribbon elements are practically completely insulated against the outside, and radiate the total amount of the in-flowing electrical energy in the form of heat toward the kettle wall and bottom.

Figure 25 shows the total assembly of an electrically heated kettle. Such modern kettles are mounted four to six feet above the ground and are not surrounded by a mass of supporting and insulating brickwork, as is the case with the old type kettles, thereby greatly reducing the fire hazard. In the picture can be seen the insulated casing, inside of which are located the electrical elements, which heat radiantly the kettle sides, bottom and top. On top of the kettle can be seen the manhole used for loading purposes; it has a sight glass, through which the reactivities inside the kettle can be watched. In the upper part of the photograph can be seen the agitator motor with its gear reduction unit and the reflux condenser, both mounted directly over the kettle. Some of the many valves visible in the picture serve to feed liquid raw materials and intermediates into the kettle, while others are used for controlling pressure, vacuum, cooling, refluxing, or to introduce steam or inert gases.

FIGURE 25.   Total assembly of electrically heated kettle.

FIGURE 26. The fuse box panel for a production kettle.

The fuse box panel, protecting the production kettle and all its accessories against electric overload and mechanical risks, is pictured in *Figure 26*.

In actual production units

the electrical input

is regulated in various ways, for instance, by installing three separate circuits, which in turn are subject to variations by means of electrical Y and $\triangle$ connections, thereby supplying a large number of different heating possibilities. *Figure 27* shows an electric distribution panel giving a conception of the neat and accurate way in which the electric heating current is conducted to its various points of consumption.

In the upper left hand corner is the main switch which opens and closes the circuits between the meter and the heating elements and electrical appliances. In the upper right hand corner is a magnetic switch, which allows the motor to be controlled from different and remote points. Underneath it, is a device to protect the motor against overload. Through the middle of the panel runs a row of thermostatic controls for the protection of the heating elements. The lower part of the distributing panel in the picture is occupied by magnetic switches, which govern the current flowing to the various positions of the heating elements. The whole panel is totally enclosed in a metal cabinet, with access to the mechanism through doors, which are normally locked, providing the highest degree of safety for the operator and workmen.

For normal purposes, relatively few amperes are sent through the heating elements, which thereby are heated only to a dark, hardly visible glow, equivalent to a temperature of 500° C., evidencing the mildness of this heating system. If quick heat transfer is required, stronger currents are necessary, which produce an orange color in the elements, equivalent to a temperature of 700° C.

Figure 28 shows electrical elements while the current is

FIGURE 27. Electrical distribution panel.

passing through. Their glow is pronounced but not strong enough to allow photographing during daylight. The picture, therefore, was taken at night with an exposure time of several hours. After obtaining in this way the picture of the

glowing heating elements

themselves, the complete casings and the surroundings were photographed in another exposure with the help of flood lights.

As the illustration shows, the heating elements are arranged in a casing designed to surround closely the kettle wall. The casing is well insulated against heat loss to the outside, the inside lining being of stainless steel. The heating elements, in the form of folded Nichrome bands or ribbons, are placed on this liner in a firm position supported by porcelain insulators.

The preferred method of today's indirect heating, based on the Dowtherm liquid, is the system which is installed by most large resin producers. Heat transfer is efficient, because of the extremely high amount of heat carried by the Dowtherm vapors and conveyed to the kettle when the vapors condense on its walls. Temperature control is accurate, because it is regulated by changing the vapor pressure of the Dowtherm liquid which is possible with a high degree of accuracy. The unusually high penetrating properties of the Dowtherm liquid make it necessary to keep a constant watch for possible leaks in the elaborate system of pipes and valves required in this heating method and, in addition, a constant watch has to be kept for possible carbonization in the pipes and the boiler unit.

The outstanding feature of

the Dowtherm system

is the possibility of extremely fast cooling. For this purpose, cold Dowtherm liquid is circulated through the heating jacket, pumped from a storage tank. The liquid is constantly kept cool through a heat exchanger and water coils.

An important consideration in all heating systems is the cost. The comparison of b.t.u.

prices of fuel or energy

is misleading, because such b.t.u. costs are only a part, and sometimes only a minor portion, of the total heating costs. In addition to the efficiency of heat utilization, other factors have an important bearing on cost figures, particularly the depreciation of valuable installations over a relatively short period of time, and the expenses of maintenance, such as re-lining of furnaces, replacing of burners, upkeep of stack, tanks and other appurtenances. Finally, heating costs also depend very much on the type of materials produced and the methods used in processing them.

All these factors have to be taken into consideration in order to arrive at reliable net cost figures and actually are reflected in the data given below, based on the production of hard coat-ing and ink resins. The figures are taken from production records and show the following costs for various heating methods, expressed in cents per 100 pounds of resin produced:

Coal	3¢
Oil	9¢
Gas	15¢
Electricity	27¢

The costs for gas heating vary according to the type of gas used, by plus or minus 10%. The cost of electrical heating is based on a resin production of five million pounds yearly. If this production is doubled, electricity costs are reduced by 20-30%, due to lower power rates. Comprising actual heat cost data per year for an annual production of five million pounds of hard coating and ink resins, the corresponding figures are

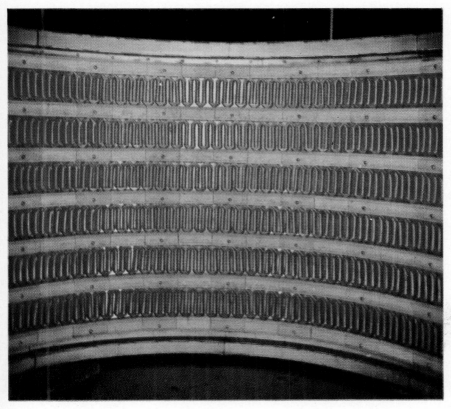

FIGURE 28. Electrical heating elements in full glow.

Coal	$ 1500
Oil	$ 4500
Gas	$ 7500
Electricity	$13500

It appears that for the specified resin production the

expenditure for electrical heating

is $12000 annually higher than for coal firing, meaning that an additional $1000 must be spent monthly on heating only, an expense which is well spent, because of the ease of operation, the perfect control, the cleanliness of the equipment, the low cost for upkeep and labor and particularly because of the greatly reduced fire hazard.

The operating costs for the indirect heating by means of the Dowtherm system depend upon the fuel used for the Dowtherm vaporizer. In order to make an estimate of the heating costs in the Dowtherm system, the figures previously given for direct heating, should be increased by 20 to 40%, to compensate for the additional costs, caused by the upkeep of the complicated equipment for indirect heating and particularly by the depreciation of this expensive equipment. Comparing the cost of direct electric heating to the cost of Dowtherm heating, based on fuel oil, the former is about twice as high as the latter.

The previously described kettle and heating equipments are adequate for all normal coating and ink resins. Special problems, however, present themselves in the production of resins with particularly high viscosity. In the case of

highly viscous resins

it is difficult to preserve their color, to prevent the formation of large amounts of decomposition products and to obtain uniformity in batch composition. Due to their high melting points and their excessive foaming tendencies, considerable hazards are involved, because the hot material may overflow from the kettle, may catch fire, and explosion may even occur. To cope with the engineering problems involved in the production of excessively foaming, highly viscous and difficult to fuse resins, the Author of this book has suggested kettle construction and equipment according to the description given in his U. S. patent No. 2,061,469, entitled "Process for Melting and Treating Organic Substances Employed in the Manufacture of Varnishes and the Like."

The handling of excessive foam as, for instance, in copal running, can be kept under control by the customary means of foam beating, if the kettle load is small relative to the total kettle capacity, *i.e.* not larger than 25% of the total because, in this case, there is sufficient space above the liquid to hold the rising foam. However, the orthodox method becomes impractical when the kettle load is increased to the extent required by the economic factor, *i.e.* anywhere between 40 and 70% of the total capacity. For such purposes, the above system suggests the use of an agitator, designed to suck down the tough and thick foam which is lying on top of the resin batch, and usually is cooler than the balance of the material. Due to this suction the foam is carried in a downward movement into the main body of the resin in the lower center of the kettle. Reaching this area, the stringy, viscous mass is heated by the surrounding medium, loses its toughness and releases entrapped vapors, with the result that the foam dissolves and disappears. The redissolved foam is then forced by agitator action from the lower kettle center in a radial direction against the lower kettle side wall, and from there on driven along the sidewalls upward into the top layer, thus completing a

vertical circulatory movement.

In addition to this vertical circulation, a certain amount of the usual horizontal, radial and tangential agitation necessarily takes place.

The defoaming treatment described, is more efficient than the customary foam beater, which attempts to break up and abate foamy masses mechanically by the cutting action of quick moving wire-like rods. It is also safer because it avoids the formation of finely dispersed matter, which may fill the empty top of the kettle in the form of a fog, and is always subject to explosion.

Various stirrer designs, available in commercial engineering, cause a downward suction in the upper center and produce a centrifugal movement in the lower part. Many of these stirrers are too weak in action. Only those are suitable which can create sufficiently strong forces to overcome the resistance of the highly viscous and foamy masses.

Another essential feature of the

foam abatement procedure

under discussion, makes it possible to apply intense heat to the upper parts of the kettle, if and when it is necessary, and achieves this effect by surrounding the top and the upper part of the shell entirely by electrical heating elements. Thereby tough foam, rising dangerously high, can be quickly liquefied and recombined with the batch. The same device prevents the vapors from condensing in the upper part of the kettle, and flowing back into the liquid contents, where it would be mixed with the resin itself and again augment foaming. The heating of the upper kettle region also helps to equalize the temperatures within the resin batch, thereby reducing partial overheating, which is one of the major causes of excessive foaming.

Resin-producing kettles are equipped with a number of accessories, necessary to insure good products. Among the more important accessories are the condensers, pumps and devices for loading and unloading.

Air and water cooled condensers are provided to reflux the glycerine during the period of esterification, with the condenser temperature regulated so that the glycerine vapors are condensed and returned to the kettle, whereas the water, formed in the reaction, is allowed to escape. Pipes, usually extending to the bottom of the kettle, are provided for the introduction of carbon dioxide, inert gases or steam, the flow of the last named materials being controlled by flowmeters. Such gases reduce the fire hazard, prevent oxidation and preserve the color of the resins.

Another important accessory is the

vacuum pump.

The plunger type pumps have been replaced by the more efficient rotary types, especially by those through which water is circulated. The water acts as a seal and at the same time carries away a substantial portion of the decomposition products escaping from the resin. Steam jet ejectors, using high pressure steam, are efficient, but are feasible only under certain conditions. Suitable pumps must be able to create a vacuum of not less than 25 inches. They are connected to the kettle by tubing leading through a catchall tank. Leaks in the kettle may draw in air when vacuum is applied, leading to fire and possibly explosion, a risk that must not be under-estimated. Compression pumps are not required for pressure reactions in the kettles, as such reactions produce their own pressure, which is regulated by valves.

Liquids, like glycerine or formaldehyde, are loaded into the kettles by rotary pumps, both of the slow or the quick feeding type. Rosin usually is fused before loading and handled as a liquid, being pumped or moved by suction from premelting tanks or heated storage tanks through steam heated or electrically strip heated pipes.

Unloading of the kettles is done either under gravity by bottom discharge or, more often, under the action of compressed gas delivered by pipes through the top of the kettles. The finished resins are either unloaded directly into drums, or first into cooling pits, then broken up and filled into barrels or containers. In the case of direct unloading, vapors escaping at the opening valve are drawn off by a suitably designed hood, which is connected with an exhaust fan and a stack. Highly viscous resins have a strong tendency to foam after being loaded into drums, a tendency with which it is difficult to cope. Certain pure phenol resins require practically instantaneous cooling action when withdrawn from the kettle, to prevent further reactions. This is achieved by a water cooled device, designed like an orthodox filter press in reverse.

There are many

hazards of injury and destruction

connected with the manufacture of high class coating and ink resins, and there are sometimes critical moments, when it becomes surprisingly clear to the production man that energy is substantially the same as matter or, speaking more specifically, that hot resinous matter is nothing but accumulated and concentrated energy which, if loosened, can exert enormous power. Such powers often lead to dangerous conditions, as in the case of heavily foaming phenolics, of rapidly reacting maleics, or of copals which are cracked at high temperature. Detailed safety measures have to be taken to provide against the dangers of injurious vapors, of overfoaming, of fire and explosion.

An important safety consideration is the proper arrangement of the total assembly of machinery and equipment, to allow free access to every unit thereby avoiding any loss of time and excluding any unnecessary movements on the part of the operator. As previously mentioned, the processing kettles must be equipped with sight glasses, to observe conditions inside the kettle, with powerful foambreakers to beat down rising foam, and must be provided with emergency overflow outlets, receptacles and valves. General safety equipment, such as respirators, masks, shields, glasses, gloves must be readily available and their use enforced to protect the working men. Fire-fighting equipment must be complete, considering particularly the usefulness of carbon dioxide, both piped to the kettle and in the form of extinguishers filled with liquid carbon dioxide. Kettles must also be connected with an efficient fume dispensing system, the vapor escape lines either leading into a separate stack, or being drawn off by ventilator suction into a cooling and condensing system. Fume incinerators have not been successful for the disposal of resin vapors.

The most important safety measure is the proper

heating and temperature control

of the resin kettle. In addition to being the primary factor for safety, it is the first condition for producing closely specified resin types. The temperature is measured at various points within the resin load, at the kettle walls and at the heating elements, at the reflux condenser, at the fume outlets and possibly other points. Mercury operated instruments have been replaced by electrical potentiometers, the thermocouples for which are placed in stainless steel pipes, sealed at the bottom. By the introduction of an automatic balancing device, potentiometers comprise indicating, recording and controlling devices in one instrument, thereby supplying continuous day and night records of the temperature. These instruments also serve as thermostats, to keep temperatures constant or, as time cycle controllers, designed to make the temperature follow automatically standard heating curves. In addition, temperature limit controls can be provided and can be set at a point slightly above the specified and safe temperature. If this temperature is exceeded, the device causes a light to flash, a bell to ring, warning the operator, or causes the heat source to be cut off immediately without the operator's intervention.

Automatic heat control marks a great technical advance. Though it is no more efficient than the human control, it exerts its control with more regularity, more perseverance and more accuracy, and has the paramount advantage that it never forgets. On the other hand, too many automatic control devices are liable to lessen the watchfulness of the kettle operators, causing difficulties in other directions.

A typical

control instrument panel

of a resin kettle is shown in *Figure 29*. The picture not only demonstrates various temperature controls, but also shows the measurement and recording of pressure and vacuum, and the

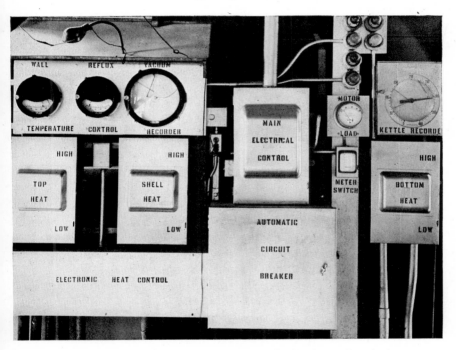

FIGURE 29. Control instruments of electrically heated resin kettle.

control of the power consumed by the agitator motor. Giving a more detailed description, on the upper left hand side can be seen the wall temperature control. This instrument shows the temperature of the kettle wall and also acts as a thermostatic safety device against overheating of the kettle. The same panel board carries the reflux control instrument, indicating the temperatures of the gases or vapors in the reflux condenser, and also controlling the temperature of the water in the jacket of the condenser.

The vacuum recorder, visible in the picture, is used to record vacuum conditions and maintain the constant vacuum required in some kettle operations. The boxes, labeled as top heat, shell heat, bottom heat, contain devices which make it possible to apply heat of various degree at different points of the kettle at the same time. The heat, thus applied, is in turn controlled by self balancing, electronic instruments.

The automatic circuit breaker, actuated magnetically, is designed to protect the heating elements against the destructive action of short circuits or overloads. The indicating lights, shown at the upper right hand side of the picture, are important for the kettle operators, because they show, at a glance, the location and amount of heat being used. The marking "motor load" is seen on an ampere meter, and shows the number of amperes of current consumed by the agitator motor, which can be interpreted in terms of the resin viscosity.

The kettle recorder shown at the right indicates, on a special dial in the form of a continuous graph, the temperature changes in the kettle, which is useful in duplication of the heating cycles of future runs. The same recorder may be designed to keep the kettle temperature constant for long time periods without manual control.

The machinery and equipment previously described, produce resins by the non-continuous processing of single, separate batches. In view of the many

continuous line production

methods in other industries, it seems desirable to replace batch processing with continuous operation in resin manufacturing. The industry of vegetable oils has developed non-stop oil bodying procedures, circulating the oils by a pump through an electrically heated system of pipes. The temperature of the oil is quickly raised, held for a definite time, and then quickly cooled. The length and the size of the tube circuit are so adjusted that the oil is bodied to the extent desired. An automatic temperature control protects against any excessive temperature rise due to exothermic reactions. In batch processing, exothermic reactions cannot be sufficiently controlled and make it impossible to body, for instance, linseed oil in large quantities at temperatures substantially higher than 305° C. The continuous process in a tubular system, however, makes it possible to raise the temperature of polymerization of linseed oil by about 20° C. without serious danger, thereby accelerating the speed of bodying to the required degree.

Possibly, following these principles, further technical developments in the resin field will lead to continuous or assembly line processes in resin manufacturing. The material will probably be conducted through a system of heated pipes, with the speed of flow regulated so as to give each reaction step sufficient time for completion, and with the apparatus designed in a manner to allow by-products to escape.

A paramount consideration in such continuous processes is the

use of catalysts

able to accelerate the resin-producing reactions. Very unique catalysts for this purpose are described in the Author's U.S. Patent 2,024,103. They are colloidal solutions of heavy metals, such as cobalt or manganese, in organic solvents, obtained by electrical dispersion. The production of colloidally dispersed metals by means of electricity is a very interesting phenomenon. It is achieved by oscillating electrical discharges of high voltage, and can well be demonstrated by a laboratory experiment with cobalt in the following manner: a glass jar, with walls sufficiently strong to withstand high tension sparking, is filled with butanol, which is the best dispersion medium, since it yields the most stable solutions of colloidal metals. The cobalt metal, to be dispersed, is placed on the bottom of the vessel in the form of metallic granules, which display a large surface and thereby accelerate dispersion. The granules are located between the ends of two aluminum wires, which form the electrodes for the electric current. This current is generated by a suitable spark conductor, which must have sufficient capacity to overcome the resistance of the butanol. While the oscillating discharges take place with spectacular sparking, cobalt metal dissolves, forming a colloidal solution of dark color. In this form the cobalt possesses unique catalytic properties.

In order to make continuous processes for resin-production possible, the use of catalysts, such as the interesting type described in the previous paragraph, will be helpful. However, many other

technical and mechanical problems

connected with continuous line production must be solved before the same high type coating and ink resins, now made in batch processes, will come from such an assembly line.

Chapter X

The Patent Situation

The knowledge of patent affairs is not sufficiently appreciated by many technical and commercial men active in the coating and ink resin field. Chemists and technicians often disregard the fact that knowledge of patent matters actually amounts to a superior faculty which thereby raises them above the level of the average technologists. Their often inaccurate knowledge of the practical operations of the patent law is one of the reasons why, in so many cases, they receive so little tangible reward for their high type of brain work. Even distinguished inventors and scientists have come to the proper appreciation of the importance of patent matters only after a long time and at the cost of some expensive blunders.

Executives in the field of surface coatings and printing inks also often underestimate the importance of patent affairs and practices, because of the confused outlook in this field. The confusion is due to the great number of patents covering synthetic resins, a number which is growing every week, and will soar continuously as a result of organized research and development work. The somewhat confused aspect is also due to the difficulty of properly

evaluating the technical and legal strength

of patents. The latter is of great economic importance, because there is always lurking in the background the danger of infringement suits, or the threat of more or less involuntary royalty payments.

It is, therefore, desirable to clarify the patent situation with regard to coating and ink resins by discussing the questions of patent quality and validity in this field, and by explaining the particular aspects of patents covering esterification, phenolic resins, rosin-modified maleics and copal-type synthetics.

The first consideration in evaluating patents must be the realization of the fact that a patent does not generally protect the basic principle of an inventive thought, but only those features of the invention which are specifically described in the claims and which are restricted in number for any one patent. The latter two factors are of particular importance for patents in the resin field. In order to protect broadly a basic inventive idea in detail, it is, therefore, necessary to describe all possible variations which can be fully done only in a string of individual patents. This very fact impairs the value of a single patent, and is one of the reasons for the uncertain quality of a majority of patents in the coating and ink resin field. In addition, there are other reasons for the existence of a

great number of poor quality patents.

There are several cases where the Patent Office has issued patents for products and processes in the field here under consideration, which actually were not new. Anticipations in printed patents are not normally overlooked; however, the amount of printed publications generally is so voluminous, that pertinent references can easily be missed by the searching examiner. Such cases have occurred, particularly at time periods when the Patent Office was overworked and undermanned. A more efficient examination might be obtained by officially appointed experts outside the Patent Office, or by making applications, after their allowance but before their issuance, open to public inspection. Such publication would give the possibility of raising opposition on the strength of prior literature or actual prior use.

Novelty is the primary requirement for patent validity. It cannot be established too clearly, because there has been no suit in the resin field in which the defendant has not declared categorically that the owner of the patent in question was not the first and true inventor.

In this connection, the paradoxical case should be mentioned that the inventor himself may stand in the way of his own invention, *i.e.* if he has described it in some publication two years prior to the filing in the Patent Office.

There are also many cases where the applicants for patents have not lived up to the

standard of inventive thought

as properly required for the benefit of patent protection, basing their application only on routine technology, merely applying existing general knowledge to special problems, or solely selecting a known material to meet known requirements, which is the all too weak foundation for a number of "use" patents in the resin field. The same is true of so many so-called "paper" patents, created simply by some one guessing what is to be the next chemical development, and covering this guess by application. The same is true of those patents conceived by analogy from other patents, through turning such conceptions into experiments and the experiments into patent specifications and claims. Most of these patents are invalid but, nevertheless, they may possess a considerable nuisance value.

Into the same class belong those defensive patents, which are taken out for the sole purpose of showing that one is not infringing on some other patents; and into the same group belong those ornamental patents, which serve as decorative matter for advertising purposes. Preparation of "paper" patents sometimes leads to grossly off-shade specifications. As

an amusing example

in the field of surface coatings, the case of U.S. Patent No. 2,343,180, issued in 1944, is cited in the following paragraph.

This patent covers a coating to be applied to glass fabric, or similar material, to make it fireproof and waterproof. The glass fabric is first given a coating of a sodium silicate solution and then treated with a coating composition, containing amyl acetate, ricinus oil, sodium nitrate, paraffin, nitroglycerine, boric acid, thinner and ether. The specification explains that in this composition each of the ingredients contributes an important characteristic to the mixture, and then enters into rather grotesque technical details. The specification argues at great length that amyl acetate affords flexibility to the dried coating and contributes to its fire protecting features, that sodium nirate prevents brittleness of the coating, and that paraffin adds tensile strength to it. The specification continues in the same vein attributing highly improbable achievements to the other ingredients, in a manner and to a degree that it must invalidate, with necessity, any claims based on such a specification.

This case shows clearly that the mere issuance of a patent by the Patent Office does not prove that the patent is valid, only because it has been issued. The legal

strength of a patent remains doubtful

until it has been tested in the Law Courts, and the probability that it will stand this test is small. To substantiate this guess of probability, the once famous Courtauld-Celanese case is cited. It was fought out in England under technical circumstances very similar to American conditions. Under the English patent law, fees have to be paid annually, and by stopping payments, patents are officially abandoned, thereby indicating their degree of strength in a legal or technical sense. Out of 667 applications made in connection with chemical subjects in the above case in one particular year, only 65 reached completion. Of these 65, all but 16 were abandoned after the first year. A further 7 were given up after about three more years, and by the time this whole case came before the Court, the number of patents which had lasted so far were two. Finally, one of these two was held invalid, so that only one out of the original 667 really survived.

On the other hand, American experience proves that good patents on good inventions, coming from good inventors, seldom become the subject of litigation, and that only doubtful cases are brought into Court for the purpose of establishing their validity. The technical, commercial, and legal conceptions, which establish validity of patents, are in a state of constant flux.

Patents have been invalidated because the inventor allegedly did not show a creative spark or

"a flash of genius"

when he made his invention. The definition of what constitutes a "flash of genius" is entirely a matter of the judge's opinion with regard to the inventor's mind. For instance, one and the same finding would be a genuine invention if made by a production man whose ordinary task is routine manufacturing, and would be nothing but a self-evident conclusion if obtained by a research man whose duty is the scientific search for new facts. The Supreme Court has clarified this situation by a statement in the printing ink decision in the Gessler patent case to the effect that the purpose of the patent system is not to hand out to the inventor a certificate of merit; consequently, it is not concerned with the quality of the inventor's mind, thereby practically eliminating the formerly important factor of "flash of genius." In fact, the patent statutes do not demand a flash of genius as a base for the patent, but nothing more or less than a new and useful invention or discovery.

Patents may be held invalid in one instance, because the substitution of one known material for another in a known combination is not considered to amount to invention, and may be upheld in another case, because the substitution steps are considered to go beyond what is obvious to persons skilled in the art, and are not ordinarily predictable.

The Courts have held that only in such cases where the inventor has discovered new and unknown properties present in a given material, or where he has found a long sought for result, which has baffled an army of skilled investigators, may the

substitution of one material for another

reach the plane of invention.

Substitution also might be considered an invention, if it was not the obvious thing to do, as shown by the fact that during many years numerous inventors have tried to achieve the effect, without hitting upon the particular substitution idea. Knowledge after the event is always easy and, in many such cases, the substitution looks so simple that everybody says, "Why, this matter is so obvious, we should have thought of it before."

Opinions fluctuate also as to the standard of inventions in patents worked out by organized and streamlined mass research. One school of thought considers this work as mere technological routine, whereas the other side states that a discovery does not lose its character as invention only because the result has been arrived at by recognized research laboratory procedure, and that there is certainly no reason why guesswork should be deemed superior to orderly and scientific research work.

Patents, totally or in part, often lay themselves open to invalidation due to the fact that the majority of their claims are broader than the invention. Often an inventor has made a specific discovery and then tries to protect this special finding by formulating claims of wide scope. This practice is very dangerous, because the patent may be held invalid for the reason that there may be hundreds of substances or methods that will answer the description of the claim, of which only very few might actually work in the way described in the invention. It is therefore good advice not to stretch one's net too far, because it might easily be stretched beyond the breaking point.

On top of these technical viewpoints, there are purely commercial factors that enter into judging patent validity because the definition of a patent also includes the realization of a practical purpose, which may lead to the paradoxical case of a patent without an apparent inventive thought. The

factor of commercial value,

for instance, was the deciding viewpoint in the well-known Duco case, dealing with the low viscosity cotton patents of Flaherty and Hitt. In this case one of the judges frankly admitted afterward that it was hard to find an inventive thought in the patent, and stated clearly that the only reason the Court decided in favor of Dupont was that, according to the conviction of the judges, the patent had a paramount commercial value, evidenced by the fact that it revolutionized the industry.

In addition to the technical and commercial viewpoints, purely legal factors may influence patent validity as, for instance, the Supreme Court decision that patents must not be used as instruments for the restraint of trade. Apparently, the individual monopoly granted by a patent is lawful if exerted individually, but if such monopolies are united to restrain competition, the danger of a violation of the

anti-trust laws

arises. This factor gains practical importance in the field of coatings and inks, when pooling arrangements and cross-licensing agreements are contemplated.

Due to the constantly changing aspects of patent validity, the outcome of patent suits is entirely unpredictable. The Lower Courts have a tendency to evade the issue of validity altogether by making decisions on the question of infringement only, or by limiting the scope of the claims involved. The Courts of Appeal may reverse the first decisions on grounds completely unpredictable by the technical man. The Supreme Court upholds very few patents that come before it, a fact that is rather saddening to the technical man. In accordance with this attitude, the Supreme Court has invalidated the Gessler heat-set printing ink solvent invention.

Additional difficulties arise from the fact that in all patent suits

expert witnesses

are of deciding influence, and that the genuine technical experts, without any strings attached to them, are difficult to secure. Therefore, instead of obtaining the help of a real specialist, *i.e.* of a man who, as the saying goes, knows "more and more about less and less," which in such a case is of the utmost importance, one must be satisfied with some one of general knowledge and little specialized training.

Another factor that renders the outcome of patent suits unpredictable, is the fact that the question of validity of a patent boils down to the personal judgment of the judge or of the majority of judges constituting the Court. Their legal minds, which have to pass upon the important technical questions, may have a rudimentary conception of chemistry and physics, but cannot be expected to fully comprehend all the chemical and physical aspects of a complicated scientific problem.

Considering the

advisability of starting a patent suit

it also has to be kept in mind that, according to general experience in the coating and ink field, any patent litigation does not strengthen the regard other people have for the dignity of patents. On the contrary, such suits have lowered patent morale, which is very deplorable in view of the fact that so many earnest workers have secured patents for which they command due respect.

The question of the approximate costs in infringement suits in the different Courts is also of importance. Considering normal costs for official business, the expenditures run in the same order of magnitude before the Lower Court, the Court of Appeals and also the Supreme Court; a lower limit of three thousand dollars can be reasonably assumed for a simple case, which requires little preparation, which remains simple and does not call for the help of eminent scientific or legal talent.

As a rule, however, ample technical and legal preparation is necessary and the case becomes more and more complicated during the proceedings, with the result that the

expenses and costs

involved will run many times the above amount, sometimes into very high figures, especially in the higher Courts.

The costs for preparatory technical work by expert witnesses, for their acting as witnesses before the Court, and for further experimental work often made necessary during the trial, depend on the time the experts are required to devote to the case, and on the degree of their professional standing, all of which is entirely unpredictable. Many of these costs are spent for no better purpose than to uphold, explain and demonstrate the technical matter which is brought into question in the trial, to the members of the Court, who seldom have more than an elementary knowledge of the scientific principles involved.

The uncertainty of costs is also true for the fees which the legal counsels charge for their work in the legal preparation of the case, the taking of the evidence, the presentation and the arguing of the case before the Court, the fees growing considerably, sometimes astronomically with the eminence of counsel.

Considering all pertinent factors with regard to starting a

patent fight in the field of surface coating and printing inks, and viewing particularly the very uncertain outlook, the old rule still stands, that it is preferable to avoid litigation, and the more so, the more formidable the opponent.

The simplest and probably the cheapest

way to avoid litigation

consists in taking out a license. Royalty agreements, both of the exclusive or the non-exclusive type, have operated to the advantage of both patent owner and licensee in the coating and ink field in a number of cases but, nevertheless, the general feeling obviously remains opposed to royalty contracts. On the other hand, it must not be forgotten that the party that is licensed under a patent, enjoys a more stable market for the product with usually better prices, and that the inventor or the owner of the patent receives the financial credit that is rightfully due to him, and that he usually reinvests the royalties in continued development work.

Exclusive royalty agreements often have an advantage over non-exclusive license arrangements for the patent owner from a tax point of view. An exclusive license to "make, use and sell" the products of a patent constitutes a sale of the patent by its owner, and regular payments received for it are considered to be capital gain, subject to a substantially lower tax rate than ordinary income. Non-exclusive licenses are regarded as a lease of the patent and royalties received from such an agreement are taxed as regular income.

It is sometimes useful to consider patents from

the accountant's point of view.

If a patent is acquired by purchase, its cost is the price paid for the acquisition. If a patent is self-developed and finally obtained by the inventor, its cost is the total of the official Patent Office expense, the fees for the attorney and the expenses spent in experimental work. The latter figure may vary within very wide limits. In the case that a legal suit has to be fought through, it is reasonable to add the costs of a successful suit to the book value of a patent, because a patent cannot be considered valid until it has stood the test of an infringement suit.

The book value of patents has to be written off over the period of its lifetime, which amounts to seventeen years for a newly granted patent. Usually the patent costs are written off in less than that time because, according to experience, the majority of patents become antiquated due to new technical developments, before their date of expiration. In cases where the products, manufactured under the patents, have proved to be unprofitable or unsaleable, as has happened in the resin field, the patent evidently is valueless and should be totally written off at once.

Discussing further the ways and means of avoiding litigation, a practical method consists in

developing an equivalent invention

which does not infringe on the other patent. This has been tried in various ways with more or less success. Infringement is not avoided if equivalent substances are used as substitutes, or if other changes are made, which suggest themselves to those skilled in this type of work. Nor can the other patent be evaded by making its method of working deliberately more complicated as, for instance, by adding extra steps or incorporating unreactive or otherwise useless matters. Infringement, however, can be prevented by simplifying the original invention, by the omission of certain steps or materials, provided the same results are obtained.

Every time a patent suit in the particular field here under consideration has been fought out in the Law Courts, the question of

patents versus trade secrets

is discussed in the trade, *i.e.* whether an invention should be kept as a trade secret or should be patented. As a rule, the products and processes in the coating and ink field, cannot easily be duplicated, but experience has shown that, nevertheless, the final duplication and imitation is only a question of time. It has to be accepted as a fact, that trade secrets cannot be kept over a lengthy period of time, because sooner or later they are either discovered by a legitimate laboratory research, or disclosed by some sort of leakage, that always seems unavoidable. The natural decision in the above mentioned question, therefore, is mostly in favor of preparing a patent application.

Following these general comments, specific questions pertaining to patents on coating and ink resins and their uses in surface coatings and printing inks have to be discussed.

From a survey of the existing patents on coating and ink resins, it appears that the form in which they are styled follow

a standard pattern

which developed gradually, and now seems to be generally accepted by patent workers. This is true at least for the majority of those which are not pioneer patents of a fundamental nature, but cover improvements of things that have been invented before. Most of the coating and ink resin patents refer to some previous work.

At first the object of the invention is broadly stated, taking care at the same time that the terminology used is clearly defined. Special reference is made to one's own prior applications or patents, if the specification is connected with the applicant's previous inventions, as it is often the case in continuous research work.

Secondly, the background of the inventive thought is described, emphasizing the shortcomings and defects of the prior products and processes and, as the third section of the pattern, those deficiences are contrasted with the advantages of the new invention. These comments supply an opportunity to specify in detail the various objects of the invention, emphasizing the particular points that are new, improved or unexpected.

As a rule, a paragraph is inserted, mentioning that the application refers to both the products as such, made according to the invention, and the methods of manufacturing them, as well as the various applications they might find in actual practice. The same paragraph also emphasizes the thought that all details are given only as illustrations and explanation, but not as limitation, stating that those skilled in the art can make changes without departing from the scope and spirit of the invention.

Then follows the essential core of the application, describing both the leading thoughts and the practical details. It is desirable to include some plausible theory on the scientific principles underlying the process. Such a working theory may aid in explaining the inventive thought to the Examiner and thereby indirectly may assist in securing claims.

In describing the invention, it is detrimental to be vague or verbose, because such defects weaken the patent, when issued, by inviting infringement. It is also poor practice to supply incomplete information, relying on the possibility of adding later on facts or statements which were not in the original application. Such insertions are invariably rejected as disallowable new matter.

As the next paragraph in the application pattern, it is customary to define in detail the important characteristics of the raw materials which can be used, and to describe specifically the possible modifications in the quantities of raw materials employed and the method of production used. Those comments often are followed by an enumeration and detailed description of the various uses to which the products of the invention can be put in practical application.

Finally, as a rule, the application quotes a series of examples of carrying out the invention, and always concludes with a

set of claims.

The examples given usually refer to the particular kinds of products or processes which are mentioned in the claims. The examples must be described with enough detail so that they actually work and give the desired results. Guesswork must be strictly avoided because it may create defects which can easily be detected by any competitive experimentor, and may render the patent invalid.

The claims are the vital part of a patent application; they are like the boundaries staked out on a piece of land by a prospector. In case of litigation, the claims are explained and read in connection with the detailed description given in the application and, therefore, should be drafted accordingly. An excessive number of claims is objectionable; it is, therefore, good practice to limit their number, although there are patents in the resin field which carry up to fifty claims.

As a rule, three different individual kinds of products or processes, as described under a generic claim, are allowed. If the application is broader in scope, it must be subdivided and divisional applications must be filed.

In formulating claims in the field of surface coatings and printing inks, it must always be kept in mind that product claims are by far more valuble than process claims, and that it is not good practice to claim products in terms of the processes employed to produce them.

Discussing technical patent questions with regard to the individual resin classes dealt with in this book, the fact has to be emphasized that the production of all coating and ink resins, with very few exceptions, includes as the essential step, the

process of esterification.

Patents on esterification of rosin or copals, either alone or together, have been in existence for many years. However, they have apparently never been considered strong enough by their owners to even try their enforcement. Such patents do not limit themselves to esterification by glycols or glycerine, but include practically all substances capable of esterifying with rosin, up to the higher alcohols and the sugars. The two oldest of these patents, U. S. 382,907, entitled "Manufacture of Artificial Copal" issued in 1888, and U. S. 501,446, entitled "Manufacture of Resin Acid Esters," issued in 1893, both to Eugene Schaal, mention specifically mannite, so closely related to the pentaerythritol family. These old ester gums had already great commercial value. *Figure 30* is the photostatic copy of the first page of an interesting old document, *i.e.* of a sales pamphlet of a New York copal broker, dated November 1894, which offers the esterified products described in the two aforementioned ancient patents. The surface coatings prepared from these ester gums obviously were of good quality, because they were used to paint the Paris Eiffel Tower.

Next to the glycerine esters, the rosin esters of pentaerythritol have attained great technical importance. They are first described in U.S. Patent No. 1,820,265, issued in 1931 and owned by the Hercules Powder Company. This patent, together with two other patents that refer to the use of pentaerythritol rosin esters in varnishes and coating compositions, has been dedicated to the public, giving any one the right to use them without any liability. The patents in question refer to esters made with ordinary pentaerythritol, but have no reference to esters which are based on one of the polypentaerythritols, separately or in mixtures.

Patent coverage in the

FROM
C. H. KIESSIG,
No. 4 GOLD STREET,
New York.

NOTES

ON THE

MANUFACTURE OF VARNISHES,

FROM

DR. EUG. SCHAAL'S ESTER GUMS.

(Patented in the United States and Canada.)

PURE AND IN COMBINATION WITH COPALS, RESINS, ETC.

GENERAL OBSERVATIONS.

The purpose of Varnishes, Lacquers, Japans, etc., is to impart to the articles to be varnished a smooth and more or less brilliant surface, and to protect them against the destructive action of the atmosphere (heat, cold, moisture, etc.), and other pernicious influences.

This protection is best obtained by the use of such materials as have the least tendency to be destroyed or dissolved by the action of rain, sun, heat, cold, dust, chemicals, etc.

As such substances are known and in general use: Resins, Waxes, Asphaltum, Fats and Fatty Oils, to which we may add Paraffine, Ceresine, India Rubber, Gutta-Percha, Nitro-Cellulose, etc. But as most varnishes, besides durability, should possess a certain degree of hardness and brilliancy, we have to consider chiefly the natural resins and gum-resins, which, in combination with fatty oils and other solvents and thinners, form the basis of ordinary varnishes. These Gum-Resins are partly of a fossil or semi-fossil nature, products of an extinct vegetation, such as Amber and several Copals, whereas others, such as Manila, Mastic, Sandarac, Damar, Shellac, Colophany, etc., are exudations of living species of trees.

Most of these Resins are of an acid nature, and not at all indifferent in the presence of metals, metallic oxides, alkalis, colors, etc.; on the contrary, they either corrode, or otherwise attack these substances, or are destroyed by them; hence the constant endeavor of the varnish manufacturer to neutralize these resin acids.

Until now this purpose has been accomplished by a treatment of said resin acids with metallic oxides, such as Lime, Magnesia, the oxides of Lead, Manganese, Zinc, etc. All these metallic combinations, however, show one general defect: They are easily decomposed by moisture and carbonic acid, and split up into hydrated oxides and the original resin acids, which latter are promptly oxidized and destroyed in the presence of oxides capable of acting as transmitters of oxygen.

All these detrimental effects are avoided by the use of **Dr. Eug. Schaal's** patented

ESTER GUMS.

These **Resin Acid Esters** or **Artificial Copals** are hard and perfectly neutral bodies obtained by the treatment of the natural resin acids with an Alcohol, such as Mannit, Glycerine, Resorcine, Wine-Alcohol, etc., under elimination of water.

The chemical nature and composition of these products are quite analogous to those of the oils, fats and waxes of animal or vegetable origin, which are likewise Esters or Composite Ethers, containing fatty acids instead of resin acids.

By the neutralization of Resin Acids with an Alcohol, very stable bodies are obtained; whereas, the original Resin Acids are soluble in Alkaline Carbonates and Alcohol, Resin Acid Ethers are insoluble in such liquids. They are also extremely durable in the presence of moisture and eminently fit for the manufacture of varnishes for ship-bottoms, damp places, etc. They resist very well the action of soap, mix with metallic paints without thickening or curdling, are good non-conductors of electricity, and protect metals against oxidation.

The **Eiffel Tower** at the **Paris Exhibition** was painted and varnished with the products of the licensees of Dr. Eug. Schaal's French patents.

Acid vapors, chlorine, sulphurous acid, etc., have very little effect upon Ester Gum, which is im-

FIGURE 30. First commercial announcement of ester gum.

field of phenol resins

is widespread and involved. A comparatively simple patent picture, however, is obtained if the field of discussion is limited to the special phenolics, discussed in this technological study, *i.e.* the pure alkyl phenol resins and the rosin-modified phenolics.

Oil-soluble pure phenol resins were first described in the British Patent No. 15,517, issued in 1905 to De Lair as the inventor, who at this early time emphasized the importance of para-substituted phenols. His resins, however, were not practicable and it took an additional thirty years before another inventor, Herbert Hoenel, hit upon the right idea, to produce soluble pure phenol resins, from para tertiary butyl or amyl phenols, which are suitable for coating and ink purposes. These interesting materials, made either by acid or alkaline catalysts, are described in the basic U.S. Patent No. 1,996,069, entitled, "Process for the Production of Condensation Products" issued in 1935 to Herbert Hoenel. This patent carries with it a disclaimer, by which all aryl-substituted phenols, aiming particularly at phenyl phenols, are excluded from protection by this patent. Resins based on the latter phenols, both of the para-substituted and ortho-substituted types, are covered by the Bakelite U.S. Patent No. 2,017,877, issued in 1935 to Victor H. Turkington.

The first rosin-modified phenolics that had sufficiently good color, light stability and solubility, were of the bis phenol type, described in the basic U.S. Patent No. 1,623,901, entitled "Method for the Improvement of Natural Resins," issued in the United States in 1927 to Amann and Fonrobert, the original disclosure actually going back to the year 1917.

Rosin-modified alkyl phenolics for surface coatings and printing inks are described in a string of Hoenel patents, applying a method of manufacturing by which the phenol compound is introduced into substantially neutral substances, mostly of the resinous ester type, as for instance, commercial ester gum. Today's methods of producing modified phenolics do not follow the technique described in the Hoenel patents, and do not esterify the rosin before incorporating the phenolic component. They reverse the sequence by first combining the phenol formaldehyde condensate with the decidedly acid rosin and esterifying afterwards.

A new principle is introduced into the manufacture of rosin-modified phenolics by the author's two U.S. Patents, issued in 1942, *i.e.* No. 2,268,946, entitled "Phenol-Modified Ethers" and 2,268,947, entitled "Phenol-Modified Esters." The phenol ether-alcohols, used for the production of the new type of modified phenolics, are characterized by the presence of additional hydroxyl groups, which are capable of reacting with rosin acids, thereby effecting a more intimate connection of rosin and phenol component than is possible with ordinary phenol alcohols. They are produced by first converting the proper type of phenols, preferably para tertiary butyl or amyl phenols, into their monomeric alcohols by reaction with formaldehyde in alkaline solution and then reacting the resulting phenol alcohols with glycerine at low temperatures under high vacuum.

There are a great number of patents in existence describing the

use of phenolic resins in varnish and ink materials.

However, the possibility of enforcing them seems doubtful for the reasons previously explained. In this connection, the example of heat-set inks, which usually contain high melting and easily soluble modified phenolics, is mentioned with special reference to the case of the U.S. Patent No. 2,087,190, issued to Albert E. Gessler in 1937, on a heat-set, quick drying letter press ink, which was mentioned previously. This patent describes an ink, based on the solution of a natural or a synthetic resin in solvents, which are selected in a way that the ink will not dry at room temperature, but will dry instantly upon the application of heat after printing. Among the available solvents, Butyl carbitol is described as being particularly suitable.

The patent went through two and a half years of court procedures, finally reaching the Supreme Court as the first litigation over printing inks ever to climb up to this point. The Supreme Court ruled that the patent is not an invention and hence is invalid because, according to its ruling, the selection of a known compound to meet known requirements is no more ingenious than selecting the last piece to put into the last opening in a jigsaw puzzle. After studying the technical details of the case, technical men may not easily agree with this summary conclusion and, particularly, might not find the comparison with a jigsaw puzzle very fitting. Even the solution of a jigsaw puzzle requires considerable ingenuity to arrange properly and join the individual pieces long before the last piece is put into the last opening. However, technical men may find an obvious weakness of the inventor's position in his admission that, after the discovery, he detected that certain narrow cuts of mineral oil are just as effective as Butyl carbitol.

Patent questions on

rosin-modified maleic resins

are all closely connected with those which refer to polybasic acid-polyhydric alcohol reaction products, usually classified as alkyd resins. Often the view is taken that, from the patent angle, the manufacture of maleic resins is basically identical with that of alkyd resins, and that patent anticipations and decisions regarding alkyds also cover maleics.

The basic patent in the alkyd field was U.S. Patent No. 1,893,873, issued in 1933 to Roy H. Kienle, and owned by the General Electric Company. During the lifetime of this patent it was used as a center around which more than 50 patents were pooled to form the legal base for the collection of license fees on the manufacture of alkyd resins. The patents covered all possible variations in production methods and all thinkable modifications in the types of acids, esters, and alcohols used, and also included clearly rosin-modified maleic resins. The patents, furthermore, covered the use of such resins in coating and ink compositions, including lacquers, pigmented coatings, wrinkle finishes and finishes for floor coverings, leather and oil cloth.

The elaborate alkyd resin license agreement was in operation for a comparatively short period of time, and died a quick death due to the invalidation of the Kienle patent by the Court of Appeals. At the same time all attempts to enforce the balance of a vast number of patents on the making and using of alkyd resins stopped immediately and entirely, which appears to be a surprisingly far-reaching effect of the invalidation of a single patent.

In declaring

the Kienle patent

invalid, the Court stated that the principle of this patent was to substitute drying oil acids for the acids of non-drying oils, the use of which was known from the Arsem U. S. Patent No. 1,098,776, and that, without any experimentation, it could be concluded, from experience and the knowledge of the prior art, that this substitution would give an air-drying product. Continuing its argumentation, the Court said that this substitution, therefore, did not constitute an advance over the prior art, sufficient to be protected by a patent, and also stated that the Kienle patent was further weakened by the fact that at the same time as Kienle, a number of other chemists hit upon the idea of substitution independently of each other and independently of Kienle. In the Court's opinion, therefore, the new development did not seem to be the merit of the patentee, but had to be ascribed to the changing conditions in the paint and varnish trade, which directed technical practice to the use of air drying glycerol phthalate resins.

As mentioned before, the manufacture of rosin-modified

maleics from the patent point of view is closely related to the making of alkyd resins and, therefore U.S. Patent No. 1,098,-776, entitled "Resinous Condensation Products and Process of Making the Same" issued in 1914 to William C. Arsem, has been considered as a pertinent anticipation for the production of maleic resins. The essential point of the Arsem patent, with regard to the question here under consideration, is its statement that an ester is formed from a polyhydric alcohol, which in this case is glycerine, and a polybasic acid, which in this case is maleic acid, in such proportions that free or unesterified hydroxyl groups remain; and that, furthermore, such an ester is then combined with another organic acid, which in this case is rosin acid, to complete the esterification, thus producing mixed esters of fairly definite composition. The

Arsem patent

is cited as a publication anticipating the production of maleic resins in one of the Court opinions, expressed in the litigation of utilizing maleic resins in nitrocellulose lacquers, details of which are described later. The Court states in this case that the resin element used in the nitrocellulose combination is exactly the type of synthetic resin the manufacture of which is fully disclosed in the Arsem patent.

However, more detailed disclosures on the making of maleic resins, with possibly new patentable features, are given in later patents; particularly mentioned are the patents on the diene resin and on the maleic-modified pentaerythritol rosin esters.

The diene resin patent, U.S. Patent No. 2,063,542, issued in 1936 to Carleton Ellis, uses the mechanism of the diene reaction as an explanation for the forming of rosin-modified maleic and fumaric resins. The theory of the diene reaction applied to the formation of maleic resins does not account for two facts, established by laboratory experiment and production experience. When rosin and maleic anhydride are combined in molecular ratios, a considerable loss of material occurs; whereas the diene reaction is a plain addition in which theoretically no material loss is sustained, and the complex formed by the chemical combination of maleic and rosin acid is in no way the type of substance which would be the result of the diene reaction. These plain facts considerably weaken the diene theory; however, inasmuch as erroneous theoretical explanations used in patent specifications do not invalidate a patent, they may have no bearing on the strength of some of the claims of the diene patent.

The manufacture of maleic rosin esters of the pentaerythritols, modified by the addition of one to nine per cent of maleic anhydride, or its equivalent, is described in U.S. Patents Nos. 2,322,197 and 2,344,194, owned by the Hercules Powder Company. Opinions on the strength of these patents are divided. One group feels that the use of maleic compounds for the reinforcement of rosin esters is common knowledge today, while another group is of the opinion that the Patent Office, before granting these patents, must have had sufficient evidence to become convinced that the improvement, obtained by the addition of maleic anhydride or its equivalent, goes decidedly beyond what was known and what normally could be expected from such additions. There is still another group which thinks that many claims of the Carleton Ellis maleic resin patents cover the same subject matter.

The outcome of a legal test of the validity of these patents in the Law Courts is unpredictable. However, one prediction can be made with absolute certainty, *i.e.* that such public Court fights will disseminate a great deal of practical information, which will induce and enable many surface coating and printing ink manufacturers to start the production of pentaerythritol rosin esters of their own. In the final analysis, such a development would lift the level of the industry.

The industry had the same advantage from the litigation of the Kienle patent on alkyd resins. Before the Kienle patent was brought into Court, phthalic anhydride resins were made by less than ten manufacturers. After it had gone through the Lower Court and the Court of Appeals, sufficient attention had been drawn to this matter and enough technical information had been spread around, that more than a hundred manufacturers had started to produce alkyd resins for their own use.

The use of rosin modified maleic resins

in surface coatings and printing inks is described in many U.S. patents, covering all imaginable possibilities, and mostly written up according to the traditional pattern. A very interesting application, however, based on a fundamentally new idea, is the use of maleics for purposes of producing steam-set inks, as described in a string of patents grouped around the basic Erickson and Thoma U.S. Patent No. 2,244,103. According to its specification, maleic or fumaric resins of high acid values are dissolved in polyglycols, the solution being the base for an ink which dries when subjected to the action of steam. The drying is due to the fact that the maleic resin is precipitated from the solution as a thin dry layer, because the glycol absorbs water from the steam and thereby loses its solvent power for the resin.

The validity of patents on the use of maleic resins in coatings and inks is subject to the many uncertainties previously discussed. Protracted litigation has established the

validity of the Weber patent

on the use of maleic resins in nitrocellulose lacquers. The history of this patent is highly instructive and enlightening on patent practice generally. The litigation centered around the U.S. Patent No. 1,722,776, entitled, "Composition of Matter, Comprising Resin Esters," which was applied for in 1922 and, after more than seven years in the Patent Office, was finally granted in 1929. It was issued to Harry M. Weber, one of the research associates of Carleton Ellis, and is owned by the Ellis-Foster Company. After another seven years the patent was reissued in 1936 as Re. 19967, the reissue specifying, in the pertinent claims, the particular organic carboxylic acids which were mentioned in the original patent specification, but probably had been originally omitted in the claims, due to inadvertence.

Patents are reissued only for the unexpired part of the term of the original patent. The reissue procedure, therefore, does not amount to

a renewal or an extension of a patent

for which there exists no possibility. Nevertheless, attempts are made continuously, with more or less success, to achieve this very result by filing, at regular intervals, successive applications which cover practically the same matter, only considered from different angles.

The Weber patent was applied for at a time when nitrocellulose lacquers were given an enormous impetus by the invention and the marketing of low viscosity nitrocellulose, which occurred between 1922 and 1926. At about the same time new solvents became plentiful and dibasic acids, useful for resin manufacture, began to decrease in price and became more readily available.

The Weber patent was finally held valid on very sound technical reasons, the Court stating that its outstanding feature is the fact that, although the resin described is a very hard one which imparts toughness to the film, it had, nevertheless, contrary to the previous experience in this industry, a very wide range of compatibility with nitrocellulose.

The Weber patent, together with other patents which expire several years later, is the object of licenses issued to resin manufacturers, who in turn extend to purchasers of their lacquer resins the right to use such resins in combination with nitrocellulose.

The patent situation in the field of

copal-type synthetics

is closely connected with the Author's string of patents on mastication of fossil gums, particularly U.S. Patent No. 2,007,333, which describes the basic principle of solubilizing copal gums. Mastication does not utilize heat to make the copals compatible with synthetic resins, but depends on mechanical force to achieve that purpose. The patent situation of copal-type synthetics is also closely connected with certain methods of incorporating free alcoholic hydroxyl groups into synthetics resins, as described in the Author's U.S. Patents Nos. 2,268,946/7, and is related to patent work on resinous polyhydric polymers, produced from hydroxy rosin esters.

Special emphasis is laid on patent development work, covering the interesting principles which are the base for the formation and the properties of copal-type resinous esters. Resinification is carried out under certain circumstances, described in a previous chapter, to build up large molecular aggregates, which is then followed by molecular degradation under controlled conditions.

The resins which can be subjected to such a polymerization and degradation cycle are rosin-modified phenolic resins, maleic resins and hard resinous esters of glycerine or the pentaerythritols. The composition of such resins may vary in type and quantity of ingredients, the deciding requirement being their ability to form a gelatinous resin on heating which, on further heating, can be liquefied again. The process is carried out by subjecting the resin gel, in an especially designed equipment, to a heating and cooling cycle with agitation, pressure and vacuum. The resulting depolymerized resin, obtained from the gelatinous resinous ester, has a higher degree of solubility, molecular homogeneity, mechanical toughness and heat stability than a polymerized resin of the same composition, melting point and viscosity, *i.e.* property characteristics, which distinguish fused fossil gums.

The previous comments convey an idea of the

manifold aspects of the patent situation

in the coating and ink field. They show that the patent literature is full of valuable technical information which must be studied seriously, before starting and while carrying out one's own patent work on new products and processes. The comments also provide a base for judging the validity of patents, so that reasonably founded decisions can be made, whether a contemplated new technical process should be covered by an application; whether this process or product could possibly infringe on some outside individual patent; and whether this particular patent can be considered to be strong enough in an infringement suit to justify royalty payments, rather than going through Court procedures.

The comments on the patent situation also supply a conception of the spirit which governs resin matters in the Patent Office or the Courts. This spirit is somewhat different from that in other technical fields, but its intimate knowledge is important for everybody who has to make decisions in patent questions.

Index